PARABLES AND FABLES

Peter Ribes SJ

Parables and Fables

30 texts for teachers
or just for the pleasure of readers
fond of "flights of fancy"

ST PAULS

ST PAULS Publishing
187 Battersea Bridge Road
London SW11 3AS, UK

Copyright © ST PAULS 1990

ISBN 085439 325 0
First published 1990. Reprinted 2000

Set by TuKan DTP, Fareham, UK

Printed by Interprint Ltd, Marsa, Malta

ST PAULS is an activity of the priests and brothers
of the Society of St Paul who proclaim the Gospel
through the media of social communication

Contents

Foreword 7

Introduction 9

1. The camels 15
2. The guitars 20
3. The caravan 25
4. Brother, let me teach you 29
5. Prakash wanted to see God 39
6. What are you doing there? 41
7. Plenty and want 46
8. The swallows 51
9. I knew it! I knew it! 56
10. We know all about it 63
11. The little fish 68
12. The begging bowl 73
13. Isaac 78
14. Can they not taste by themselves? 83
15. Autobiography of a coconut 89
16. What's the trouble, Mr Toiler? 95
17. Thou shalt not have other gods before me! 99
18. Margaret 105
19. Listen to the greyhounds 111
20. A monkey business 116

21.	The Samaritan's predicament	124
22.	A spidery world	131
23.	The cows	136
24.	D–n it!	143
25.	What would you call it, mum?	149
26.	God's judgement	155
27.	Eureka!	160
28.	The floating country	166
29.	Uncivilised!	172
30.	Glasses and lenses	178

Foreword

There was a time when nearly all wisdom was expounded and passed on in purely intellectual terms of reference. Efforts were made to interpret biblical parables as a means of understanding more about life's mysteries. Today we seem to have rediscovered the value of "speaking in parables", as Christ did himself. The greatest master on earth must have had some good reason for teaching in parables, using simple, everyday things to express eternal realities. Parables, fables, allegories, even fairy tales are always very popular, especially among young audiences.

Parables have a power of expression far beyond ordinary speech or carefully worded rational arguments. Anyone whose mind is attuned to symbol and imagery will find more "truth" in a parable than in a learned doctoral thesis! Let us not forget that "knowledge" is one thing and "truth" quite another. One has to do with an accumulation of facts, the other with wisdom.

Parables have also a power to stir the "public conscience" and to rouse people from their state of torpor or complacency. Parables sharpen the "intuitive" eye of the mind – "clay-shuttered", to use a poetic expression – by our modern day excesses of logic and rationalisation.

Parables help us to see things, not merely to understand them. They put us in touch with the "core" of reality, they lead us straight to the "heart" of truth.

This book was prepared at the National Vocation Service Centre, in Pune, India, where parables were used during training sessions for teachers and students from Seminaries and Religious Formation Houses. Such parables proved to be a stimulating means of encouraging active discussions and a sharing of ideas.

For convenience, the parables in this book are grouped under three headings:

(i) religious values – (religious themes);
(ii) personal values – (psychological growth, personality);
(iii) social values – (conscientisation, social themes).

Most of the parables, however, do not belong exclusively to one category. Many embrace all three and may therefore be used during sessions devoted to apparently different themes.

Each parable is contained in a chapter which contains:

(i) the text of the parable;
(ii) messages of the parable;
(iii) ideas and application of the parable; and
(iv) references to biblical texts in keeping with the ideas of the parable.

All these parables were originally prepared as "scripts" for audio-visual montages, role-playing and mime. This will explain why they have been given their own particular format, style and development.

Introduction

VALUE OF PARABLES

Transcultural

Languages are normally shaped by the influence of various cultures. "The language" of parables is not conditioned by any particular culture.

The parable's original language may change with the passage of time but its message remains unchanged.

Parables transcend cultural frontiers. They have a universal value. The Gospel parables, for instance, are valid everywhere.

The message of a parable is not affected by the medium of its presentation, whether this be audio-visual, a drawing, a painting, a piece of music or whatever. The message comes through alive and intact, however the parable may be presented.

Timeless

Parables are relevant always and for all time. They touch upon and evoke something primordial and fundamental in the human race.

They are always old and always new. They speak to us in the depths of our being, untrammelled by what is happening, either on the surface of our lives or according to the ebb and flow of events around us.

Symbolic

Parables share in the nature of symbols.

They are not confined to mere words. They are a kind of "non-verbal" communication.

Parables can be expressed without words. They can be the subject of mime, acting, drawing, song or dance.

Parables address themselves to everyone – literate or illiterate, learned or ignorant, trendy or old-fashioned. But they yield their secrets more readily to those unspoilt by "culture" and "civilisation".

Parables speak an idiom far more direct, incisive and eloquent than ordinary speech. While other words remain opaque, parables are translucent.

Subversive

Parables challenge the established order, social structures and value systems. They smash our idols. They debunk the hypocritical self-complacency of everyday life, the conventions by which we rationalise our social pretensions, the mechanisms by which we try to protect our pampered ego.

They open our eyes to the many distortions of our "social order", caused by injustice, oppression and exploitation on the one hand, and by a glaring lack of social concern and commitment on the other.

Provocative

Parables prod and provoke, challenge and chasten, awaken and activate.

They force listeners to react, to re-interpret and re-evaluate our behaviour, thought and emotional patterns.

They shock us into reform and renewal.

They rouse us from self-delusion and lack of true purpose.

Sounding board

Parables hold up a mirror to life, compelling listeners to understand their own lives more clearly by relating them to the stories. Through these stories, they see themselves for what they are and not what they pretend to be.

Parables are sounding boards which help inner attitudes

to come to the surface, making it easier to find the vision of reality which shapes or should shape our lives.

Reactions to the parable stories show whether a listener is making an honest attempt to face reality boldly or is trying to cover it up with a curtain of illusion.

Prophetic and proclamatory

They "proclaim" what should be acceptable and what should not.

They urge a change of heart as the basis for any radical transformation of one's life.

They reveal the inmost depths of the person in whom may be found God, who is love itself and the answer to all human conflicts.

They disclose God's ultimate fidelity to those sincerely striving to know and do his will, even when they know nothing of what it means for them or where it will lead them.

USE OF PARABLES

General principle

Parables are not "gap-fillers" or "time-killers". They are not meant to entertain people or dangle some attractive distractions before them. They are meant to be "starters" or "triggers" to provoke the audience to act, react or interact. They are only the beginning of a process of reflection, discussion and sharing.

Hints for teachers and group leaders

(a) Be quick to pick up reactions of the group and of each member in particular.
(b) Be very alert and sensitive to the emotional vibrations and moods of one and all.
(c) Tune in to the "wavelengths" of your listeners.
(d) Accept them as they are.
(e) Keep going along with them. Do not force the pace.

(f) Start from where they are and then lead them on as far as they go, in the direction of where they should be.

Ways of Presentation

When you want to use a parable for any type of session, begin with the most impressive way of presentation available to you. Given below are 13 different modes of presentation:

1. *Read* the parable to the audience.
2. *Distribute printed or duplicated copies of the parable* and ask the participants to read them very carefully.
3. *Narrate* the parable yourself or invite a good story teller to retell it.
4. Invite the participants to *read it in dialogue form*.
5. Have it *mimed*.
6. Have it *acted* – as either drama or burlesque.
7. Use *puppets*.
8. *Radio-play technique*: prepare a taped sound-track and replay this to the audience.
9. *Shadow-play*.
10. *Photo-language*: picture or photo-story technique.
11. *Poster story*: participants prepare posters beforehand and use these to explain the story.
12. *Live tableaux*: keep building the tableaux as the story proceeds.
13. Show an *audio-visual montage* based on the story.

Before the presentation

– Prepare your audience by creating a suitable mood of seriousness and willingness to co-operate.
– Explain that the parable is being presented in order to encourage discussion.
– Encourage an attentive but relaxed attitude.
– Encourage the audience to enter into the mood of the parable, willing to be swayed by it.
– Insist on strict silence before and during the presentation. Ask participants to reserve any comments until later.

–   Do not announce the title of the parable, describe its contents or disclose its theme beforehand.

After the presentation

Time for reflection
–   Don't be in a hurry to start the sharing or discussion.
–   Keep the group in a state of reflective silence for a while.
–   Ask the group to remember the main points or scenes of the parable and to dwell on the feelings and insights acquired at the time of presentation.

Sharing and discussion
–   After a period of personal reflection, invite the group to share and discuss.
–   You can conduct the sharing and discussion in either of two ways, whichever you may choose: the Open Method or the Restricted Method.

Personalisation
–   Allow the participants to reflect in silence on the implications, for their personal lives, of what was discussed and shared.
–   A simple questionnaire may help reflection and personalisation:
    • Any insight or awareness about myself?
    • Is there anything I should change in my life?
    • Am I happy to be what I am? Why?

Setting goals
–   Ask the participants to take one step, however small, towards implementing some change in their behaviour.
–   Ask them to write down both the step to be taken and the means chosen to implement it.

Prayer
–   Invite the participants to pray, either as individuals, in small groups or in one single group.

1

The camels

Horace looked up to the sky and said to his friends:

"What a fantastic star! I think it's beckoning to us and asking us to follow it."

They all lived near an oasis, where their lives were peaceful, simple and secure. They always had lots of grass and dates to eat and plenty of water to drink.

Nothing ever seemed to disturb the placid existence of these camels but they now sensed that their friend was certainly fascinated by the strange, bright new star. It puzzled them and they wondered what it could mean.

"I remember one of my dreams as a child", continued Horace. "I saw a star rising over the horizon and clearly heard it beckoning everyone to follow in search of a new life, a new country, a new fatherland... I wonder if this could be the same one."

Some of his friends now laughed at him. Those who hadn't seen the star called him a mad visionary, a foolish dreamer. Those who had seen it called him crazy:

"What? Follow that star? Nobody's ever thought of that before! Where? How? For how long? Why follow it at all?"

"Where? Wherever it may lead!" he answered, "and for ever, if we need to. Because it's inviting us! I feel drawn towards it, helplessly... I'll follow it, whatever it may cost. I've made up my mind and nobody can ever stop me!"

Most of the other camels left him alone and went back to eating, drinking and sleeping.

Only a few stayed behind. They were intrigued, both by the new shining star and by the way it seemed to have completely taken over their friend. One of them asked:

"Do you mean to go out into the desert, Horace, and leave all the comfort and security of this beautiful oasis?"

"Yes. I've decided to give everything up. Look! It's starting to fade from our horizon. I'll have to hurry up! If anyone wants to join me, you're welcome! But delay is dangerous. Come on! One minute more and the star could pass us by. It might disappear and never come back. It's now or never, the chance of a life-time!"

A few camels were certainly impressed with Horace's eagerness and determination. They made up their minds, there and then, to join him:

"We'll come as well! But give us time to get some things together for the journey. We need plenty of grass, lots of water, dates and grain. We need…"

"Look, time's running out! The star's moving away. We can't wait a minute longer! The one who's calling us to follow him surely won't do so without seeing to our wants. He'll look after us during the journey. I'm leaving at once. Anyone who wants to join me, come along. If not, stay behind and fend for yourselves!"

He started walking away from the oasis and into the empty, friendless and never-ending desert. His eyes were glued to the little shining star as it steadily vanished from the horizon over the oasis.

Only two camels ran and joined him, before it was too late. All the others shook their heads in disapproval and muttered:

"They're crazy! They're bound to die of hunger, thirst and exposure. And to think they could have stayed here with us, in the oasis, enjoying all the good things life can offer!"

GENERAL SUGGESTIONS

Messages of the parable

- The meaning of a Christian vocation.
- We must have enough generosity to say "Yes" to God, whenever he calls.
- God's demands are absolute and constant.
- If we cling to what we have, we shall never be able to follow God or share in the rich life he offers.
- We have no lasting city here and life is a pilgrimage.
- In order to follow Christ, we must empty ourselves of all that we have.
- Growing in trust and confidence in God's providence.

Ideas and applications of the parable

- Life – Christian life in particular – is a journey. We have to keep moving.
- We firmly believe that we are going somewhere. Where are we going? How far have we progressed? Where are we now? We just believe there is a "somewhere".
- Ideals are a prime necessity of life. To move on, we have to dream the *impossible*, the unpredictable.

- Courage to be *ourselves* and to follow our consciences.
- Courage to be different, to swim against the tide, to resist a temptation to follow the world's changing fashions and crazes.
- We cannot afford to play safe. A Christian must willingly give up worldly security.
- Inner impulses, the movements of grace and God's inspirations.
- In the service of God, we cannot be too rational. God is not an Aristotelian deity!
- Rationalisations are the opposite of rationality! We would do better to abandon our intellectual pretensions and look for God with hope and love in our hearts in the midst of uncertainties.
- We rationalise not what is true but what we "want" to be true.
- We have to leap in the dark to reach the light.
- We have to trust God implicitly. He leads us "somewhere".
- To enter into possession of "The All", we have to forego "Our All".
- Meanwhile, we have to raise our eyes to heaven in prayer and silence.
- Attachments enslave us... they immobilise... freeze us... They stunt our growth.
- To grow, we must constantly become dead to our "todays" and be born again into our "tomorrows".

Bible texts in keeping with the ideas of the parable

Gen 12:1-4	The call of Abraham.
Ex 3:1-6	The call
Ex 3:10-12	of Moses.
Jer 1:4-10	The call of Jeremiah.
Mt 2:1-11	The Magi.
Mt 2:13-15	Joseph and the flight into Egypt.
Mt 4:18-22	Jesus calls his disciples.
Mt 6:24-34	Do not worry. God will provide for you.

Mt 9:9	The call of Matthew.
Mt 16:24-26	Whoever wants to save his life…
Mk 10:17-31	The rich young man.
Lk 14:25-33	Cost of
Mt 10:37-39	discipleship.
Jn 12:22-25	Unless the grain of wheat dies…
Acts 9:1-18	The call of Saul.

2
The guitars

A new folk-group didn't seem to be enjoying much success until one night a member of the audience suggested the guitars needed tuning. On reflection, this seemed wise advice, since all these guitars had been bought second-hand and were usually stored in either very damp or very dusty rooms.

Various tuners were contacted through the Yellow Pages and the least expensive one was given the job. He arrived within minutes and eagerly set about the work.

Taking hold of the first guitar, he began pulling and tensing its strings.

"Ouch! Hey! Ow! Ooh!" yelled the unfortunate victim.

The other guitars heard and saw what was happening and they all became terrified. One of them whispered to his friends:

"Just look at him. He's a sadist! He seems to enjoy making people suffer."

All the guitars were now shaking with fear but the tuner took no notice and continued working with an apparently pitiless lack of concern.

Meanwhile, in the far corner, half-hidden under a cushion, Adolfo, one of the smaller guitars remained frozen with fear, deliberately trying not to move:

"Please God! Don't let him find me. Save me from this torturer and I'll do anything you ask!"

Adolfo's prayers certainly seemed to be answered. The tuner failed to notice him as he still lay motionless underneath the cushion:

"Thank you, God, for sparing me", gasped the grateful little guitar.

In the evening, the musicians arrived, ready for their next engagement. As soon as they began trying them out, they were delighted:

"These are fantastic now! I can hardly believe they could ever sound so good."

The guitars, of course, felt very flattered and proud of themselves.

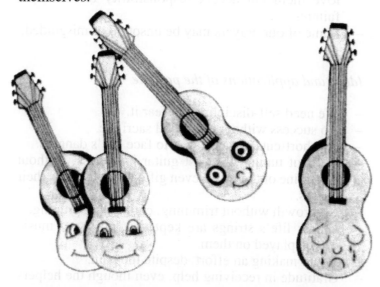

Then one of the guitarists noticed Adolfo sticking out from under the cushion. As soon as his strings were pulled, everyone groaned. Then they all started laughing:

"What a croak! It's a right duff guitar, this one. I think we'll give it a miss for tonight at least."

They all picked up the other guitars and went back downstairs. Poor Adolfo was left alone. He felt insulted and began crying:

"Nobody likes me. I'm useless."

GENERAL SUGGESTIONS

Messages of the parable
–   The meaning of suffering.
–   Nothing can be accomplished without suffering and
    pain.

- Most failures are due to our fear of or aversion to effort, sacrifice and self-discipline.
- Identifying the "tuners" in our lives, we can learn to love them but accept responsibility for our own failures.
- Some of our prayers may be unsound or misguided.

Ideas and applications of the parable

- We need self-discipline but fear it.
- No success without effort and sacrifice.
- No short-cuts, no easy way to face life's dangers.
- Without tuning, the best guitar is useless. Without discipline of the spirit, even gifted people waste their talents.
- No growth without trimming, cutting and pruning.
- Unless life's strings are kept taut, no sweet music can be played on them.
- Joy in making an effort, despite the pain.
- Gratitude in receiving help, even though the helpers cause us pain.
- Those who love us make us suffer. Do not curse the tuner but kiss his hand.
- God is life's great tuner. We must bless him in adversity and pain.
- He knows what is best for us and can bring the most melodious music from the most unpromising instruments.
- Pray not to avoid suffering but for the courage to suffer and to persevere.
- Often we pray like the "scared" guitar but then feel self-pity at failure.
- No use crying over lost opportunities. Let us seize the ones to come and make the best of them.
- The easy option of blaming others when we fail to change ourselves.
- Honesty and courage to accept responsibility for our own failures.

- Kindness but firmness with those in our care, not leading them to think that success comes easily.
- The folly of shielding people from the pains of development. Progress is achieved through suffering.
- Duty of tuning others, helping them to produce the sweetest music.
- Avoidance of all "paternalistic", "maternalistic" and "protectionist" attitudes. We must help people to bear their suffering, not "rescue" them.

New Testament texts in keeping with the ideas of the parable

Mt 5:10-12	Persecutions and suffering. Be glad! Great rewards wait for you.
Mt 10:16-23	Coming persecutions. You will be saved.
Mt 13:44-46	The hidden treasure and the pearl of great price. Sell all you have to secure them.
Mt 16:21-23	Peter remonstrates against suffering. Jesus calls him Satan.
Mt 16:24-26	To save your life, you must lose it.
Mt 26:36-46	The agony in the garden. Jesus had to suffer.
Mk 9:30-31	Christ announces his impending sufferings.
Lk 4:1-13	Temptations in the desert. Jesus renounces comfort, honours and power. The great "pruning".
Lk 24:13-27	Emmaus: "Was it not necessary for Christ to suffer and thus enter into his glory?"
Jn 12:22-25	"Unless the grain of wheat falls into the ground and dies...."
Jn 15:1-2	God prunes every branch that does not bear fruit.

Jn 16:19-22	"Your sadness will turn into gladness… A woman at childbirth is sad… Afterwards she rejoices…"
Phil 2:1-11	Christ was exalted because he suffered.
2 Cor 11:30	Paul glories
2 Cor 12:9-10	in his sufferings.
Phil 3:8-11	All gains are loss.
Col 1:24	"I rejoice in my sufferings."
Rom 8:16-18	All sufferings of this life are nothing in comparison.
1 Pet 2:19-21	By suffering with Christ
1 Pet 4:12-13	and like Christ,
1 Pet 5:10	we shall also rejoice like him.

3

The caravan

A desert caravan was painfully making its way through dry, dusty and sometimes rocky terrain. Its members all had implicit faith in their guide, confidently leaving all decisions to him. They were especially pleased when, because of the intense heat during the day, he decided they would travel only at night and sleep during the day.

One night, during a particularly exhausting journey, the guide suddenly cried out:

"Halt! We'll stop here for a moment. As you can feel, we're crossing some pretty rocky ground at the moment. I want you to bend down and pick up as many stones and pebbles as you can find. If you fill your bags with them, you'll be able to take them home. Right, come along then," he continued, clapping his hands, "you've only got five minutes before we move off again."

The travellers, who had only been looking forward to a long rest and another sound sleep, thought their guide had gone mad.

"Stones?!" they said, "What does he think we are? A pack of camels or mules?"

Only a few of them did as the guide had suggested, putting a few handfuls of stones into their bags.

"Right, that's it", said the guide. "Off we go again!"

While they continued their weary way during the rest of the night, everyone was too weary to bother speaking but they all still wondered what their guide's strange orders had meant.

When the sun rose over the horizon, the caravan halted again and all the tents were pitched. Those few travellers who had picked up some stones were now able to look at these for the first time. With gasps of amazement, they began shouting out:

"Good grief! They're all different colours. They're all glittering and sparkling! In fact, they're *precious* stones and gems!"

But this feeling of elation soon gave way to one of gloom and despondency:

"If only we'd had the sense to carry out the guide's orders and fill up with as many stones as we could carry."

GENERAL SUGGESTIONS

Messages of the parable

- Awareness of life as a journey.
- Acceptance of life's hardship and suffering.
- The meaning of hardships and sufferings.
- Trust in Christ as our leader on life's journey.
- As a pilgrim people, we must support each other along the way.
- Courage to go through life with joy, peace and hope.

Ideas and applications of the parable

- Human life compared to a journey through a desert.
- Life's journey towards the Kingdom of God.
- Where is that Kingdom? When shall we arrive? It doesn't matter. It's enough for us to know that we shall arrive one day.
- Faith and hope sustain us.
- We must press on, not give up. We cannot just camp anywhere we like.
- We do not walk alone but as a people, leading and leaning on one another.
- Christ is our leader. He entered into our history to lead us forward.
- He knows the destination. We simply need to follow.
- As a man, Christ shares our human sorrows, frustrations, uncertainties.
- Christ as ground of our faith and anchor of our hope.
- The Church is a pilgrim people following Christ as Leader and Lord.
- Refusing to follow Christ is to invite futility.
- In the name of Jesus we must accept and overcome whatever hurdles are in our path.
- Christ tells us to pick up his cross and follow him. Do we complain that we have enough crosses of our own?
- No apparent meaning in suffering but a need to obey our Guide and fill our bags with crosses.
- Crosses, sufferings and sorrows will, one day, be understood.
- All will be transfigured, crosses transformed to resplendent joys. We shall regret not having accepted more.
- If we sow in pain, we shall reap in joy.
- Death and resurrection are two sides of the same coin. Glorious resurrection is impossible without the ignominy of crucifixion.
- God sustains our courage by occasional glimpses of his Transfiguration.

- Hidden value in suffering: those who discover it give up all they have to acquire it.

New Testament texts in keeping with the ideas of the parable

Mt 2:13-14	Flight into Egypt. (On a journey).
Mt 2:19-23	Return from Egypt. (On a journey).
Mt 5:10-12	Rejoice when they persecute you.
Mt 13:44-46	The hidden treasure. The precious pearl.
Mt 16:21-27	He who wants to save his life will lose it.
Mt 17:1-5	The Transfiguration.
Mk 9:30-31	The disciples cannot understand the doctrine of the Cross.
Mk 10:32-34	Jesus explains the doctrine of the Cross.
Mk 8:31-33	Peter remonstrates.
Lk 2:1-20	Birth of Jesus, in poverty, despised and in pain.
Lk 4:1-13	Temptations of Jesus. He despises riches, honours and power.
Lk 5:1-10	In your name, Lord... Following orders.
Lk 12:13-21	The rich fool.
Lk 12:32-34	Riches in heaven.
Lk 24:13-35	Emmaus: "Was it not necessary...?"
Jn 3:14-16	Nicodemus: "The Son of Man has to be lifted up."
Jn 12:27-33	Suffering brings glorification.
Jn 16:19-22	Pangs and joys of child-bearing.
Acts 5:27-41	The disciples rejoiced that they had to suffer for Jesus.
Gal 6:14	I glory in the cross of Jesus.
Phil 3:8-11	I count all loss for the sake of Christ.
Rom 8:16-18	The suffering of life cannot be compared with the...
2 Cor 4:10-17	The present tribulation works for us.
1 Pet 4:12-13	If we partake of the sufferings of Christ.

4

Brother, let me teach you

According to an ancient Sufi tradition, dervishes could reach the summit of contemplation by the repetition of a certain mantra or sacred prayer. The mantra in question was "YA HU, YA HU". If repeated often enough, not only would it lead to the summit of contemplation but would even enable a dervish to perform miracles and achieve such extraordinary feats as walking on water.

One particular young dervish, whose sole aim lay in attaining the pinnacle of contemplation but who was regarded by many as simple-minded, decided to leave his native village. Living all alone on a rock in the middle of a lake, he began earnestly repeating the mantra day and night.

Being so simple and illiterate, however, he mispronounced "YA HU, YA HU". Instead, he cried out "U YA HU, U YA HU", much to the annoyance of a considerably older and wiser dervish living nearby, on the banks of the lake.

"I really ought to go and help this young dervish", thought the older man to himself. He therefore rowed across the lake and spoke to the young dervish sitting on his rock:

"My dear young brother, night and day I have heard you mispronouncing our sacred mantra. I'm afraid you will never reach the heights of contemplation unless you allow me to teach you. Don't say 'U YA HU, U YA HU', but rather say just, 'YA HU, YA HU.'"

The young dervish was delighted, thanking his brother profusely and promising to heed his advice.

While the older dervish was rowing back across the lake, feeling very pleased with himself for doing such a good deed, he was suddenly dismayed to hear once more the mispronounced mantra ringing out from the direction of the rock: "U YA HU, U YA HU". He stopped rowing, wondering what he should do next but feeling especially irritated at people who remain so stubborn and cling to their old ways.

As he looked up in utter frustration, he was confronted by a most unusual sight. There was the young dervish walking towards him on the water. Reaching the boat, he bowed humbly and asked:

"Excuse me, brother, and please forgive me for being so simple but could you please tell me again how the sacred mantra should be pronounced. I really am stupid and I've forgotten the words again. Should I be saying 'U YA HU, U YA HU' or 'HU YA HU, HU YA HU'?"

GENERAL SUGGESTIONS

Messages of the parable

–   In prayer, the all-important point is the attitude of the person praying.
–   Simplicity of heart, rather than great knowledge.
–   Prayer finds many paths to God. No path is superior to another.
–   Dangers of "spiritual pride".
–   No "ulterior motives" in praying to God. (The old dervish wanted extraordinary powers.)

Ideas and applications of the parable

–   Methods and techniques of prayer are good but secondary.
–   They do not work automatically.
–   The need for suitable means to pray, without being tied to them. A slavish adherence to techniques and formulae leads to mechanical prayer, not to a true raising of the mind and heart to God.
–   Rituals and formulae are not "absolutes" but only crutches to support our faltering steps. Sooner or later they must be discarded and God encountered in utter nakedness of spirit.
–   Dangers of making a fetish of the mere mechanics of prayer.
–   God cannot be reached through humanly contrived methods, rules or techniques.
–   God gives his grace to whomsoever he wishes and by whatever means he chooses.
–   The right attitudes (young dervish) to reach God are:
    • Never think oneself superior to anyone.
    • Refuse to stand as a "master" in the presence of God.
    • Approach God child-like, with simplicity.
    • Communicate with God through the heart, not the mind.
–   The wrong attitudes (old dervish) are:

31

- Selfish, ulterior motives; personal gains.
- Pride, thinking oneself superior, misjudging others.
- Complacency, self-satisfaction with one's own prayer and good works.
- Self-sufficiency, believing we reach God by our own prayer technique.

Lessons we learn:
- God exalted the humble and confounded the proud.
- The "ignorant" can teach lessons to the "learned".
- By growing in the ways of God, we are freed from slavish dependence on methods and techniques.
- Experience teaches the best means to attain God.
- Dangers of imposing on others personal ideas about or experience of God.
- Respect for religious experience of others as the most valid in an individual life.

*New Testament texts in keeping with the ideas of
the parable*

Mt 5:1-11	The Beatitudes: blessed are the simple, the humble, the poor.
Mt 6:1	Pray and
Mt 6:16-18	fast in secret.
Mt 6:5-16	Prayer: Jesus teaches attitudes, not techniques.
Mt 7:1-5	Do not judge others.
Mt 7:21-23	Not everyone who says, "Lord, Lord..."
Mt 11:25-26	God shows to the simple and to children what he does not show the learned.
Mt 15:15-20	What comes from the heart makes a person unholy.
Mt 18:1-5	Who is the greatest before God?
Mt 21:14-16	Children praise God best.
Mt 23:1-12	Warning to those standing as teachers, masters and lords.
Mt 23:13-28	Jesus condemns hypocrisy.

Mk 12:41-44	The widow's mite. The heart is what counts.
Lk 1 & 2	God speaks to the humble: Our Lady, Elizabeth, the shepherds, Simeon, Anna.
Lk 6:41-42	"Please, brother, let me take that speck out of your eye."
Lk 18:9-14	Jesus confounds the proud and extols the humble.
Lk 1:46-55	Canticle of Our Lady.
Jn 9:1-41	The "blind" who are humble will see, the proud who can see are "blind".
1 Cor 1:27-29	God chooses the foolish and confounds the wise.
Phil 2:3	Let nothing be done by vainglory.
Jas 4:6	God extols the humble
Jas 4:10	and resists the proud.

5

Prakash wanted to see God

Prakash was a holy man and very proud of being a holy man. Longing to see God, he was obviously delighted when God spoke to him in a dream: "Prakash, do you really want to see me and possess me?"

"Of course I want to", replied Prakash eagerly. "That's the moment I've been waiting for. I'd be content even with just a glimpse of you!"

"So it will be, Prakash. On the mountain, far away from everybody and everything else, I shall embrace you."

Next day, Prakash the holy man awoke excitedly after a restless night. The sight of the mountain and the thought of seeing God face-to-face almost caused him to rise from the ground.

Then he began to think anxiously to himself about what he could take to God as a present. Surely God would expect a present but what could he possibly find worthy of God?

"I know", thought Prakash to himself. "I'll take him my beautiful new vase. It's priceless and he'll be delighted with it... But I can't take it along empty. I'll have to put something in it."

He thought long and hard about what to put in his priceless vase. Gold? Silver? Diamonds or other precious stones? After all, God had made all these himself and was therefore worthy of a much more valuable present.

"Of course!" he thought at last, "I'll give God my prayers! That's what he'd expect from a holy man like me. My prayers, my help and service to others, my almsgiving, penances, sacrifices, good deeds..."

Prakash now felt so happy to have discovered exactly what God would expect and he decided to increase his prayers and good deeds and to make a very special record of them.

During the next few weeks, he recorded each prayer and good deed by placing a shiny pebble in his vase. When this was full to the brim, he would take it up the mountain and offer it to God.

Eventually, with his precious vase filled to overflowing with shiny pebbles, Prakash set off for the mountain. At every step of the way, he continued rehearsing what he would say to God:

"Look, God, do you like my precious vase? I hope you do. I'm sure you do and that you'll be delighted with all the prayers and good deeds which I've spent so much time saving up to offer you. Please embrace me now."

Prakash continued hurrying up the mountain where he had his appointment with God. Still rehearsing his speech and now trembling with expectation, he arrived panting at the summit. But where was God? Nowhere to be seen!

"God! Where are you, God? You invited me here and I've kept my word. Here I am but where are you? Don't let me down. Please show yourself."

Feeling full of despair, the holy man flopped to the ground and burst into tears. Then suddenly he heard a voice booming down from the clouds:

"Who's that down there? Why are you hiding from me?

"It's not you, Prakash, is it? I can't see you. Why are you hiding? What have you put between us?"

"Yes, God. It is. It's me. Prakash. Your holy man. I've brought you this beautiful vase. My whole life's in it. I've brought it for you!"

"But I can't see you. Why do you have to hide yourself behind such a huge vase? We'll never see each other at this rate! I long to embrace you, so throw it away. Get it out of my sight! Throw it away! Topple it over!"

Prakash could hardly believe what he was hearing. Break his precious vase and throw away all his shiny pebbles?

"No, God. Not my beautiful vase. I've brought it especially for you. I filled it with all my…"

"Throw it away, Prakash. Give it to somebody else, if you like, but get rid of it! I want to embrace you, Prakash. I *love* YOU!"

GENERAL SUGGESTIONS

Messages of the parable

- God loves us unconditionally.
- Our willing acceptance of God's acceptance.
- Cleansing of any "Pharisaic" attitudes about observing the law or about "legal", "juridical" and "canonical" holiness.
- Excluding empty "ritualisms" and "formalisms" from relationships with God.
- Awareness of our total unworthiness before God but of his love, forgiveness and blessing which can never be merited. They are all gifts.
- Preparation for "experiencing" God's love not by doing things but by just humbly waiting for it.

36

Ideas and applications of the parable

- Entry into the possession of God demands surrender of self and all good deeds into his hands.
- Our attitude to God should be one of "worship" and "adoration".
- Advancement towards God requires us to do less but to trust him *more*.
- We have to do good deeds (wrongly called "meritorious actions") not as a means to buy God's love, which is already there for the asking, but just to show him our own gratitude and love.
- Acknowledge and accept our weakness and sinfulness with sorrow, yet free from guilt, with hope and not with despair.
- Compulsions, obsessions, scruples betray a greater trust in our good deeds than in God's infinite love and mercy.
- Good deeds may turn into idols, standing between us and God. We may worship them rather than God for whom we are supposed to do them.
- We create our own idols as protection against God's anger.
- Unconscious use of good deeds as an insurance policy.
- God loves good and hates evil but he loves us regardless of our good or evil actions. He loves us not for what we do but for what we are. If we are at all, it is because he loves us.
- In the service of God we are supposed to enjoy real peace, happiness and serenity. Anxiety, disquiet and fretfulness are not of God.

New Testament texts in keeping with the ideas of the parable

Mt 20:1-16	The workers in the vineyard.
Lk 5:27-32	The call of Matthew.
Lk 7:36-50	Jesus and the sinful woman in Simon's house.
Lk 15:1-32	The lost sheep, lost coin, lost son.

Lk 18:9-14	The Pharisee and the publican.
Lk 19:1-10	Zacchaeus.
Lk 11:37-52	Jesus accuses the Pharisees and the teachers of the Law.
Mk 3:13-19	Jesus calls his disciples – the ones he wanted.
Mk 7:14-23	What makes a person unclean.
Jn 8:1-11	The woman taken in adultery.
Jn 21:15-19	Jesus and Peter.
Rom 2,4,5,9,10	Justification is not by good works.
Gal 2:15-21	Justification
Gal 3:1-29	is a free gift
Gal 4:1-7	of God.
1 Thess 5:9-11	God has chosen us to possess salvation through Jesus Christ.

6
What are you doing there?

Mr Inquisitive spent most of his time investigating other people's lives. One day, he approached a building-site and asked one of the workers what he was doing.

"Can't you see what I'm doing?" said the rather surprised workman. "I'm working here like a donkey, carrying bricks up and down this scaffolding, thousands of times a day! Would you like to work here?"

"Oh no, thank you", Mr Inquisitive assured him.

"I bet you wouldn't", continued the workman. "It isn't worth it. Soaked to the skin and shivering in the winter, sometimes sweltering like a grease spot in the summer. I'm fed up but there's nothing else for me to do."

Mr Inquisitive then walked along the road towards Luigi's Restaurant: "Good morning, Signor Luigi, what are you doing?"

"What does it look like? I'm sick and tired of doing the same things day after day – spaghetti, tomatoes, spaghetti, onions, spaghetti, Chianti bottles to arrange, spaghetti, pans to wash, spaghetti, peppers to grind, spaghetti... I can't stand it any more!"

"What's he doing?" interjected Luigi's wife who had just come into the kitchen. "I'll tell you what he does. He helps me around the kitchen, all right. Oh yes, he helps me to eat plenty. And those greedy *bambini*..."

"But that's marriage, I suppose", ventured Mr Inquisitive.

"Marriage? A husband like that's enough to convince people there's no happiness in marriage for very long! If you're thinking about getting married, save yourself the trouble."

Mr Inquisitive didn't feel like hanging around much longer and hurriedly walked back down the street. Before long, he was asking a little boy:

"And what are you doing there, sonny?"

"I'm on my way to school. Handing in a pile of homework I can't understand. Hours and hours every night, just to please a few stupid old teachers. If you get it wrong, they shout at you; if you get it right, they say you must have copied it."

Poor Mr Inquisitive hurried off again but he still couldn't help putting yet another question to someone else.

"What am I doing here?" replied the bewildered passer-by. "I'm making another delivery of sand and cement, hard core and gravel. I do this all day long. Some days are better than others but it's always very tiring. At least, at the end of the week I get paid and that makes me happy. It keeps my wife and children happy as well. They do so much for me, so all this work's really for them. They're worth living for, don't you think?"

"Oh yes", said Mr Inquisitive, "I'm sure they must be." He then hurried off once more to see if any other people were like that and decided to interview another lady.

"Excuse me, Mrs Hutchinson, I hope I'm not interrupting your work."

"Of course not."

"What exactly are you doing?"

"I'm doing what most mothers do. Cooking for my husband and children. They seem to enjoy my cooking."

"But don't you get bored", enquired Mr Inquisitive, "doing this every single day?"

"Perhaps it is a bit monotonous but I actually enjoy doing it for people I love. Life's really worth living when I do it for them."

Then Mr Inquisitive noticed young Jimmy Hutchinson sitting at the kitchen table.

"Hello, Jimmy, what are you doing?"

"I'm doing my homework."

"Wouldn't you rather be out playing with your friends?"

"I suppose I would", replied Jimmy, "but Mum and Dad want me to study, so I please them by studying."

Feeling now much happier himself, Mr Inquisitive decided to return to the building-site in search of other happy people. One workman certainly said he enjoyed what he did. He pointed to a high tower he was helping to build:

"I'm building a church for God."

"But don't you find it very tiring?"

"It's tiring, all right, but just think how happy I am to be helping so many people to come and pray. It's great to be working for God!"

41

Although he was so touched by these words, they were still not enough to dissuade Mr Inquisitive from going through another door, where he found an obviously very poor woman singing. Asking her why, he was amazed at her reply: "Because the kitchen's my place of worship. I'm singing here for God."

"Here, in the middle of the kitchen! And you don't find it boring?"

"Of course not. I love cooking for my husband and children. I also try to make them grow with God's grace and to become truly living members of the Church in to day's world. In my own little way, I'm happy to do this and that's why I sing while I'm doing it."

"But what sort of church are you talking about?" continued Mr Inquisitive, still puzzled.

"You still don't understand, do you? My kitchen is the church. My house, the town, the world are the church."

"Ah, now I see…", said the bewildered Mr Inquisitive as he walked out of the house, wondering whether the woman was really in her right mind. But, enough for one day. He decided to return home without asking any more questions.

When he saw a young man standing under a street lamp and reading a book, he could not resist just one more question:

"What are you doing under that street light?"

"I'm getting ready."

"Ready for what? For some exams?"

"Yes, exams", replied the young man, "but much more also. I want to build a better world for everybody. I'm building the Kingdom of God on earth."

"Are you quite sure? The Kingdom of God?"

"Yes, if I don't start doing something now to build God's Kingdom, I'll certainly never do it later."

"But how can you study in such poor light?" interrupted Mr Inquisitive. "It must be a great strain."

"When I know that somehow, somewhere, some day, someone will become what I was born to be, other things don't matter."

42

"But how do you *know*? How do you know what you were born to be?"

"My heart tells me", concluded the young man. "I believe it and, if I follow what it tells me, the world will be happier and I'll know that I've really lived."

GENERAL SUGGESTIONS

Messages of the parable

- Happiness depends on attitudes and values.
- The need to find meaning in life.
- Full meaning is found in living one's vocation.
- All are called to build the Kingdom of God on earth.
- Life must be lived for others, not just for oneself.
- God is worshipped in spirit and in truth. The whole world is his temple.

Ideas and applications of the parable

- Without ideals, life is a desert, aimless drudgery.
- Happiness is not in what we do but in what we are. An occupation may be a source of joy to one but of misery to another.
- We cannot change the circumstances of our lives but we can change the way we look at them.
- We cannot always do what we like but we can like what we do.
- Living only for oneself is hell. Living for others and for God becomes a source of joy.
- Vocation means to live for God and for others, doing what we have to but with love.
- Vocation means to be the sort of person I am meant to be and to love it.
- Everyone has a vocation to be some sort of person doing some sort of task in life. Only acceptance of this will lead to understanding and satisfaction.
- All characters in this fable had a vocation. Some discovered it. Others did not.

- No-one is left out of God's plan. The Church of God needs to be built by architects, supervisors, labourers, various craftsmen but also married people, priests, teachers, clerks, doctors, missionaries, sailors – all doing, loving and enjoying what they have to do.
- Circumstances, abilities, opportunities, coupled with God's inspiration, can show people what their vocation is.
- Within my limitations, I must *"actualise"* my potentialities for building the temple of God.
- The whole earth is my temple. A desk, a sales-counter, a steering-wheel are all altars of God in that universal temple of creation.
- Each of us needs to identify our own altar, where and how we can worship God.
- Some of the people in the fable had human values which gave meaning to life. Only religious values can give the *"ultimate meaning"*.
- Lasting, unshakeable happiness and fulfilment depend on this *"ultimate meaning"*. Human values cannot suffice.

New Testament texts in keeping with the ideas of the parable

Mt 1:18-25	Joseph's life and example: happy carpenter.
Mt 4:18-22	The call of the first four disciples: to be fishers of men.
Mt 5:1-10	The Beatitudes: ideals, values, attitudes of Christ. They can make our lives happy and meaningful.
Mt 5:13-16	We are salt and light, wherever we are placed.
Mt 6:5-8	Let us do our duty quietly. God knows
Mt 6:16-18	what we do. By doing it, we build his Kingdom.
Mt 13:33	By being what we are meant to be, we become like leaven.

44

Mt 19:16-22	To be happy, we have to serve God and man.
Mk 12:41-44	The widow's mite. Let us do even the little we have with love and joy.
Lk 1:5-25	Zechariah and Elizabeth, simple pious people.
Lk 1:57-66	They did what God wanted them to do.
Lk 1:26-38	Our Lady: her simple happy life, doing God's will.
Lk 2:22-52	Life in the Holy Family: Nazareth was their temple.
Lk 17:20-21	The kingdom of God is within you. You are the Kingdom of God.
Lk 19:1-10	Zacchaeus wasn't happy with money but found happiness serving God and others.
Jn 4:19-24	The whole world is God's temple. He has to be worshipped in spirit and in truth.
Jn 18:36	"My Kingdom is not of this world." It is the world, however, within us.
Acts 2:43-47	Life among
Acts 4:32-35	the believers: joy, happiness.
1 Cor 12:12-31	We are all part of the Kingdom.
1 Pet 2:4-9	We are all "living stones" of God's Kingdom, priests of his temple.

7

Plenty and want

Two tiny islands faced one another across the sea. One, called Plenty, was fertile and produced an abundance of fruit and golden grain. The other, called Want, was rocky and barren, with scarcely any water, fruit or grain.

The inhabitants of Want were all poor, finding it extremely difficult to eke out their miserable existence. Among the inhabitants of Plenty was Mr Concern, who often climbed a little mountain to look across at Want. A kindly man, he was filled with pity, wondering to himself:

"How can those poor people survive there, let alone live? Here on Plenty, we have all we need and could afford to share everything with Want. I think I'll go across and invite them to join us."

Mr Concern hurried down the mountain and dived into the sea. He was a strong swimmer and, within three or four hours reached the desolate shore of Want. The islanders soon gathered round him, surprised that any stranger should want to visit them. They asked him what he wanted.

"I've come to invite you all to swim with me back to Plenty," he replied in a kindly voice. "There you'll be able to share with us the great wealth which our fertile island has produced. I need to rest for a while now but, in the morning, I hope you'll all go back with me."

The elders of Want met to discuss Mr Concern's proposal and it was soon agreed that everyone should accept his generous invitation. Next morning, at first light, they were all ready to dive with him into the sea.

Some of the inhabitants of Want brought with them small bags, into which they packed their most precious possessions, coins, sparkling stones and pieces of jewellery. After strapping these bags to their shoulders, they began excitedly to follow Mr Concern across the sea.

When he found himself once again back on his island of Plenty, he was both relieved and delighted that his mission had succeeded. He joyfully began counting his neighbours from Want as they followed him ashore.

Then, to his horror, as he totalled up the final count, he realised too late that the only ones to have swum across were children and others who had no bags strapped to their shoulders. Everyone else had drowned.

GENERAL SUGGESTIONS

Messages of the parable

This parable can be interpreted in two different ways:
(a) Spiritual – God's plan to save us from sin and death.
(b) Social – A new social order, according to the values
  of the Gospel.

(a) *God's redemptive plan*:

- God calls everyone to life, to the fullest life.
- Christ was love personified, God's loving concern for us.
- We live in want: no grace, no love, no hope.
- Christ lived in the divine plenitude, God's life.
- Concerned for us, he came into the world to share our want and call us to share in his plenitude.
- First he became one of us and then made his own life ours, so that we can share his life in plenty.
- To enter into a life of plenty, we must become "poor in spirit", willing to renounce all we have, to become "childlike", "trusting", "humble".
- We must follow him, plunge into the sea, braving dangers for his sake.
- In this sea, just a few miles apart, plenty is very close to want but difficult to reach.
- Like Christ, we must show concern for others and risk our lives for them.
- Only those who gave up all they had (the poor and the children) reached the land of plenty. All the others perished under the waves.

(b) *A new social order – a new faith*

- Want symbolises our world of poverty, privation and exploitation.
- Plenty symbolises the new society we want to build on love, justice, freedom.
- Those who have plenty must be ready to share with those who want.
- Everyone, whether in plenty or in want, must undergo a conversion of heart.
- Both rich and poor are attached to worldly wealth, status, prestige, fame.
- We must become "poor in spirit", "child-like" to build our society of dreams.
- To enter the new Kingdom of Plenty, we must dispossess ourselves spiritually.

- Greedy, possessive hearts will never enjoy the blessedness of plenty.
- Transformation so as not to be possessed by what we possess.
- For Christ, material want and destitution were evils but he preached a superior kind of spiritual poverty.
- The Old Testament sees riches as a blessing which could be a curse if tainted with greed and avarice.
- Mr Concern was rich but "poor in spirit". Some poor people in Want were "rich in spirit". Attaching themselves to what little they had, they were unfit for the Kingdom of Plenty.
- A new society of plenty for all needs new hearts, detached, simple, poor, child-like hearts.
- Such a society will have plenty for each one's need but not enough for anybody's greed.
- A just and equitable socio-political order is impossible unless hearts are rescued from the "want of selfishness".

New Testament texts in keeping with the ideas of the parable

Mt 5:1-11	Beatitudes: the value system of Christ.
Mt 6:19-21	Do not be greedy for earthly riches.
Mt 6:24	You cannot serve both God and money, mankind and money.
Mt 9:36-38	Jesus shows concern for the crowds.
Mt 15:32-33	Jesus worries for the crowds.
Mt 19:13-15	Jesus shows concern for children.
Mt 22:34-40	We cannot love God without loving human beings.
Mt 25:31-46	Concern for others means love for God.
Lk 7:11-16	Naim: Jesus feels pity for the widow.
Lk 10:29-37	Jesus is "Mr Concern", the Good Samaritan.
Lk 12:13-21	The rich fool. Greed for money.
Lk 15:1-32	The lost sheep, lost coin, lost son... Concern.

Lk 16:19-31	Those lacking concern cannot enter the Kingdom of God.
Lk 18:18-27	The rich young man, attached to money, is unfit to be a disciple.
Jn 1:1-14	The Word was made flesh.
Jn 3:1-21	Nicodemus. God loved the world and sent his Son.
Jn 10:1-16	Jesus the Good Shepherd, dying for his sheep.
Jn 11:25-26	I am the resurrection and the life.
Jn 17:20-26	Jesus prays for us that none may be lost.
Rom 1:18-32	Our spiritual "want", "spiritual poverty".
Rom 5:1-11	God's salvation is for all.
Rom 6:1-14	Christ came
Rom 10:1-21	to save all.
Gal 5:16-26	Conversion of heart: we have to become spiritual people.
Eph 1:3-21	God's plan to save us in Christ.
Phil 2:1-11	He became one with us.
Jas 5:1-6	Warning to the rich.
1 Jn 3:11-18	Love one another.

8

The swallows

The days were growing shorter and colder. The swallows felt an urge to fly away in search of warmer lands, where the sun would shine longer. They decided to leave this now desolate landscape, where flowers were dying and trees becoming bare.

"Fly away to somewhere else?" queried one of the wiser swallows. "Why do we have to leave this place here?"

"Because we have to find a warmer place, where we can nest", chorused some of her friends.

But the wise swallow still wasn't convinced: "How far away is this warm land you're all talking about? And how long do you think it'll take to fly there?"

The others couldn't say for certain but they insisted they must leave as quickly as possible before it was too late.

"Surely you can't expect me to leave this beautiful nest I've made here, just to go away on the off-chance of finding somewhere better?" continued the wise and thoughtful swallow, still thinking out her strategy in a rational manner, refusing to be swayed by the instincts of her friends.

"Well, we obviously can't convince you", said one of them, "but we're going to leave straight away. Deep down, we've all felt the call and our hearts keep telling us to go. I'm afraid we'll have to leave you behind, if you won't come along and join us."

The rational swallow still refused to move. After the others had gone, she continued to convince herself that she had done the right thing. It would have been madness to trust merely to inner feelings, without any positive evidence. Besides, she could make her comfortable nest even warmer and very soon she had collected more

feathers and pieces of wool to insulate it against the dangers of colder weather.

Proud of her refurbished nest, she settled down to resist the onset of winter, still believing that the others had been stupid to fly away without knowing definitely where they were going. Her extra insulation would surely keep her safe.

And so it proved to be, despite the even shorter days and increasing cold nights. Then it suddenly began to snow but still our rational and deep-thinking swallow remained cosy within her warm nest. Finally convinced she was safe from the clutches of winter, she wondered if her friends had been so lucky on their tiring and unpredictable flight into the unknown.

As the snow continued to lie, food was now becoming scarce. Not a crumb, nor a worm could be found. She grew weaker, more and more listless and eventually was reduced to no more than feathers and bones. Just as the snow was beginning to melt and a few buds started to appear, the swallow's life finally ebbed away.

Her stupid and irrational friends, who had known no better than to obey the inner voices of their instincts, returned a few weeks later. Happy days awaited them once more but their rational friend, shrunk and withered, lay dead in her cosy nest.

GENERAL SUGGESTIONS

Messages of the parable

- The need for "discernment" in finding the will of God.
- The meaning of "discernment".
- Learning to read the signs of the times.
- Trusting our feelings and accepting ourselves as we truly are.
- Dangers of "rationalising" whatever does not fit into our rational categories and yet which still makes sense.
- Obeying the will of God sometimes requires us to leave our "cosy nests", vested interests, the little world of our egos.
- The search for our vocation in life.

Ideas and applications of the parable

- Vocation is a call from God manifested through the signs of the times, the promptings of our nature and the inspirations of grace.
- Our vocation may require us to leave our "nests", country, loved ones.
- The dispositions most conducive to following a vocation are generosity and a sense of daring.

53

- To stay put in our "nest" spells ritual stagnation, a cowardly withdrawal from the struggle between the powers of life and death.
- The "voice of God" calls us to break loose from self-interested and self-enclosed living.
- Security is not the be-all and end-all of life. If a life is anything at all, it is adventure and risk.
- So-called security must be traded for the insecurity of opportunity, heart-break and challenge to the human spirit.
- The *status quo* is an idol to which we sacrifice our future and the will of God, preferring death to life.
- God speaks in many ways, not always through human language or rational argument. His ways of speaking are:
  - Our nature, even our bodies.
  - Our feelings and emotions.
  - Circumstances of our lives.
  - Signs of the time: historical events.
  - Promptings of grace – inner touches and inspirations.
- Rational arguments engage the mind. Total truth engages the whole person.
- We often use our "reason" to insulate ourselves from God.
- We rationalise in order to prove ourselves right, in order to "feel" right.
- Rationalisation is irrational, failing to realise that neither God nor human beings are designed with logical connections and functional parts neatly fitted together. This would be a denial of freedom, love and grace.
- We must learn to trust our natures and feelings, not to "rationalise" them.
- If we grow humbly but naturally, we have no need of "rationalisation".

Bible texts in keeping with the ideas of the parable

Gen 12:1-4	The call of Abraham: "Leave behind..."
Ex 4:19	God summons his people to leave Egypt
Ex 12:51	behind and set out.
Mt 2:1-12	The Magi set out in search, following the star.
Mt 2:13-15	Joseph told to flee
Mt 2:19-23	with Mary and the child.
Mt 4:1	Jesus is led by the Spirit to the desert, to the Jordan, the start of his ministry.
Mt 4:18-22	The call of the disciples:
Mt 10:1-4	"Follow me!"
Mt 9:9	Matthew: "Come, follow me!"
Mt 10:34-39	"Whoever loves his father or mother... more than me! Leave behind all you love... and follow me."
Mt 24:32-33	Lessons of the fig tree: reading the signs of the times.
Mk 10:17-22	The rich young man: "Sell everything and give it away... and follow me."
Lk 9:57-62	The would-be followers of Jesus put conditions to him.
Lk 12:54-56	Understanding the times: "When you see clouds..."
Jn 20:24-29	Thomas, the doubter, wanted proofs.
Acts 17:16-33	Paul in the Aeropagus: the Greeks wanted proofs.
1 Cor 1:18-25	Jews want miracles, Greeks wisdom.
Acts 9:1-19	Paul's conversion, surrendering all to Christ.
Phil 2:1-11	The example of Christ, dispossessing himself of all.
Rom 8:1-17	The Spirit of God versus the spirit of the world. Discernment.
1 Cor 2:12-15	The sensual man versus the spiritual man. Perception.
Phil 1:9-11	Knowledge and understanding.
Col 1:9-10	Spiritual wisdom and understanding.

9

I knew it! I knew it!

Caesar Augustus had ordered a census throughout the whole empire. This meant that Joseph would have to travel to Bethlehem and register himself. Because of the condition that Mary was in, he obviously couldn't leave her behind but how could he possibly afford to make her journey comfortable? With the baby due any day now, she certainly couldn't be allowed to walk very far. But all he could afford was a donkey.

The donkey itself was only skin and bone. It had never been treated well by any of its previous owners but it now sensed that things were looking up. Its new owners fed and washed it, even patted it sometimes. It now began to feel a sense of peace and joy coming from this happy couple. Although it couldn't explain why, it felt that this wasn't just an ordinary couple:

"I might be only a donkey", it thought to itself, "but I'm sure there's something so different about these two that they must be a bit more than just ordinary human beings."

When the three of them arrived in Bethlehem, worn out by days of weary travelling, they couldn't even find any lodgings. The donkey was suddenly brought down to earth again by the way one of the inn-keepers spoke to Joseph. After becoming used to its kind new owners, it was now reminded of how most human beings seemed to treat donkeys. Some of them treated other human beings just as badly:

"Push off! There's no room here and I don't care where you go, so long as it's as far away from here as possible!"

The only place they could find was a smelly old stable but, even then, they weren't made very welcome. The animals already living there were extremely rude to the donkey. One of the cows was especially sarcastic:

"See how lucky we are to be with such well-to-do

people who could afford a mount like that! Have you ever seen a more beautiful or more intelligent-looking donkey than that? And such a sweet voice! I'm sure it'll soon sing us a lovely lullaby and make us all sleep soundly till morning."

The horses, dogs and oxen all laughed, staring hard at the intruders.

The next few hours may have been rather more peaceful when eventually the animals did, in fact, settle down. All were quiet and most of them asleep when, on the stroke of midnight, Mary's baby suddenly arrived. Even this, thought the donkey, took place without too much fuss and nobody could complain about any undue noise or disturbance until suddenly, shuffling in from the nearby fields, came a crowd of shepherds.

Somehow they seemed to have heard about the new baby. They gazed at him and then began bowing down, saying such strange things as, "Hosanna! Welcome, Saviour! Hail! Blessed be Christ our Lord! Praise to our Messiah!"

The other animals grew really angry and one of the horses told the shepherds to be quiet:

"Look, you ignorant lot of peasants. That's a bunch of beggars you're talking to. Saviour, Messiah, Lord, my foot! He's only just been born and he won't have much of a future with those two. They couldn't even afford anything better than that stupid donkey there."

The donkey now felt extremely annoyed, not just for the insults against itself but because its kind owners and their baby were being totally misrepresented. Deciding to add its own voice to those of the shepherds, it brayed out to the best of its ability:

"Hosanna! Welcome, Saviour. I know you're all these things and much more."

"Don't be stupid", snapped one of the dogs. "How can you possibly think a baby like that is the Christ? He hasn't even got any proper clothes!"

"Because it's true", answered the donkey. "I'm certain of it."

"Certain?!" chorused two of the oxen. "Donkeys don't have brains, so how can you be certain?"

"All right, I may not have any brains but I feel it in my bones. I know this baby is our Saviour. I just know it! I know it! I know it!"

"Shut your faces, the lot of you", growled the biggest dog. "It's senseless arguing with an idiot like that, so just let's all go back to sleep."

The other animals did as they were told and the donkey also decided not to argue any more. It simply continued to say over and over again, inside its head, that this baby was the Messiah which all human beings had been waiting for:

"I know I'm not very clever and I know I have no brain, but I know that many things are truth which I can't understand. I feel it in my heart and that's enough for me. I know it, I know it, I know it..."

Many times, during the next few years, the donkey recalled that night.

Thirty-three years later, the baby Jesus had grown into a man. Some people now called him a prophet, a miracle worker and it was quite commonplace to hear him called some of the names which those first shepherds had used in the stable: Saviour, Messiah, Christ.

He had recently arrived just outside Jerusalem, where crowds of people were waiting to welcome him and carry him triumphantly into the holy city. They were expecting him to make a dramatic announcement about who he really was. His followers had palm leaves ready for the procession. They would throw these and some of their clothes on the ground, so that the procession would walk on them. They wondered how the procession would be arranged and by what means Jesus would agree to be carried in triumph.

"Go into the next village", Jesus said to one of his friends, "and you'll see a young donkey tied to a tree. Untie it and bring it back here. I want to ride on a donkey so that everyone may know that I am their Saviour, their Messiah, their Lord."

When the people eventually saw Jesus sitting on his donkey, riding triumphantly into the city, they cried out:

"Hosanna! God bless the king who comes in the name of the Lord!"

Various animals who witnessed this scene looked enviously at the stupid little donkey who seemed to have become the centre of attention:

"Why has our Saviour and King chosen to ride on a donkey of all things?" asked one horse to another. "Are we not more intelligent, more respectable and honourable than that ridiculous little pack animal?"

The donkey continued to walk forward, happily carrying its precious passenger. At every step it nodded to the onlookers, as if agreeing with everything they were shouting. And all the time it repeated inside its head:

"I knew it! I knew it! I knew it!"

GENERAL SUGGESTIONS

Messages of the parable

- In matters divine, reason is not sufficient.
- God is grasped with the "heart" and not with the "brain".
- We must strive after an experience of God.
- True God-awareness is needed among those who seem to know a lot about God but who do not *know* God.
- "Doctrines", "creeds" and "dogmas" do not satisfy as much as a subjective experience of God.
- In our encounter with God, a wholistic and integrative experience is more rewarding than rational, logical, non-personal and abstract affirmations about him.

Ideas and applications of the parable

- The simple, poor and despised are first to understand the mysteries of God.
- God showed preference to the poor and down-trodden when he wanted to disclose himself to us.
- We must become like little children if we want to enter the Kingdom of God.
- Reason abstracts from reality, giving only parts, views, aspects of reality.
- Concepts give part of the truth, not the whole truth.
- Our minds dissect, freeze, fossilise aspects of reality and tend to present them as the whole truth.
- Reality cannot be comprehended in its entirety by our tiny minds.
- Our minds are only a small part of reality.
- The "heart" takes in reality in an existential sweep. By "heart", we mean the whole reality of human beings: physical and psychological make-up, intuition, imagination, gut-feeling.
- We *know* with the "heart" many things we cannot rationally prove; we can prove with our minds many things we do not know.
- Children recognise friends and enemies, who loves them and who does not. Yet they cannot prove it. They just know.
- In every genuine encounter, human or divine, we only know what we experience. We experience with the totality of our being. Our minds do not experience a thing but only work on what has been experienced by us.
- God is not an object of knowledge but the subject of religious experience, an object of faith.
- We can *know* but cannot *experience* God with our minds.
- Relationship with God is gauged by how much we love him, not by how much we know about him.
- The "heart" holds the key to the "heart of truth".

New Testament texts in keeping with the ideas of the parable

Mt 1:18-25	Jesus's parents, poor and simple people.
Mt 5:3-10	Beatitudes: the blessings of the Kingdom are for the poor and simple.
Mt 9:35-36	Jesus feels pity for the poor and the simple.
Mt 11:4-6	The disciples of John the Baptist. The poor are preached to.
Mt 11:25-26	God reveals the mysteries of the Kingdom to mere children, not to intellectuals.
Mt 12:22-23	There is no end to arguing with
Mt 23:1-36	the Masters of the Law and Pharisees
Jn 5:19-45	that will make them understand the
Jn 6:41-59	mysteries of the
Jn 10:22-42	Kingdom of God.
Mt 16:13-20	Peter came to know of Christ as the Son of God, not through his reasoning but through his heart.
Mt 18:1-5	It is the children who best understand the mysteries of God.
Mt 19:23-15	It is they who know
Mt 21:15-16	how to praise God.
Mt 21:1-11	Jesus's triumphant entry into Jerusalem riding on a donkey.
Mt 25:31-46	Our final relationship with God (Last Judgement) will be established by how much we loved, not by how much we learned.
Mk 7:14-23	The "heart" makes us good or bad.
Lk 1:26-38	The Annunciation: Mary understood with her heart.
Lk 1:46-55	The *Magnificat:* it is the poor and simple who are exalted.
Lk 2:8-20	The shepherds, Anna, Simeon could grasp

Lk 2:25-38	the mystery; not Herod, not the Scribes and Masters of the Law.
Lk 2:51-52	Mary pondered all these things in her "heart".
Lk 5:1-11	It was Peter the fisherman and
Lk 5:23	the Good Thief
Lk 5:39-43	who could *know* Jesus.
Jn 1:43-51	Nathanael and the blind beggar came
Jn 9:1-9	to *know* Jesus.
Jn 3:1-21	Nicodemus, the Master of the Law, could not understand.
Acts 17:16-34	At the Aeropagus all rational arguments did not help Paul to "prove" the mysteries of Christ to the Greeks.
1 Cor 1:18-31	God confounds the wisdom of the wise
1 Cor 2:1-16	and the knowledge of the learned.

10

We know all about it

Some very intelligent goats heard about the Taj-Mahal of Agra and decided to go and see it for themselves:

"It isn't enough just to hear about it", one of them said. "We need to compile our own study of it."

After setting out with all their field apparatus, they were delighted quite soon to see a signpost on the road, bearing the inscription "Taj-Mahal".

"Here it is, right in front of us!" they yelled. "In all its splendour and beauty", added the expedition's Director. "We'll set up camp immediately."

The most learned and scholarly of the goats soon had their various teams organised, urging them to begin, without delay, their work of patiently collecting all the data which would benefit their own and many future generations. Whole libraries would eventually be filled with all the prodigious facts which they were about to record.

Indeed, after many months of painstaking research, they were ready to publish vast quantities of amazing statistics:

The surface of the Taj-Mahal measured	2,221,401 sq mm
It weighed	221,432,202 mg
Sand used in its construction numbered	136,541,464 grains
Particles of cement numbered	3,202,432,001
Water in the concrete slab still not evaporated by the sun	23,456,325,405 molecules
At time of reckoning its age was	78 yrs 3 m 2 wks 4hrs 5 mins

Further data concerned the structural and functional qualities of the Taj, such as its resistance to cyclones, earthquakes and other natural calamities, including lightning, its impermeability to moisture, its ability to radiate cool under conditions of severe heat.

"Thanks be to God", announced the Director, at the conclusion of their final consultative meeting. "We are all justifiably proud of our research, now knowing that we know all that can be known about the Taj-Mahal. No one can teach us any more about it. Our knowledge is unsurpassable, complete, perfect, infallible and immutable. For ever and ever. Amen."

GENERAL SUGGESTIONS

Messages of the parable

- We must approach God with humility.
- Beware of "dogmatism" and "doctrinal pronounce-ments" in matters divine.
- God is the only "absolute". Holy Scripture, dogmas, doctrines, etc., are not ends but means to come to the knowledge of God.
- Our knowledge of God will always be imperfect, tentative, relative.

Ideas and applications of the parable

- Holy Scripture and dogmas are pointing fingers, signposts, showing the way.
- We should not stop at them. The signpost was not the Taj. We must look beyond the signpost to the reality.
- Danger of "absolutising" knowledge of God enshrined in dogmas, doctrines and formulae of worship. This would turn instruments into idols, making them obstacles in our path to God.
- Extrinsic formulations of faith (doctrine, liturgy, etc.) are necessary but only tentative expressions in human language of knowledge and experience of God.
- Like all language, they are culturally and historically conditioned, relative and imperfect means to a knowledge of God.
- Such means increase our comprehension of the Divine mystery but never exhaust it.
- Theological statements have to be reworded to suit constant historic-cultural changes. This is termed "inculturation" or "transculturation".
- We can never say, "We know all about God. No one can teach us anything new."
- God and reality are too immense for the puny capacity of any person, culture or system of thought to comprehend. We cannot fit God into creaturely "moulds".

- "Idols" placate our "unbelief", "dogmas" cover up our "ignorance".
- We "sacralise" things so as to lull ourselves into a feeling of "security".
- We may follow the Church's commands and prescriptions not because we believe them right and true but because we need to feel ourselves to be right and true.
- We find it easier to deal with rituals and dogmas than to relate intimately to an almighty, inscrutable God. God is neither dogma nor doctrine. Worshipping him is not a ritual and obeying God is more than keeping commandments.
- We bring God down to human level by a kind of easy legerdemain, reducing him to dogmas, rituals and commandments.
- Finding it unbearable to stand naked before God, we clothe ourselves with beliefs, practices and rituals.
- Without realising it, we put ourselves first. God takes second place, becoming a means for us to find peace and security, not an end in himself, the absolute, for whom and by whom we live for his own sake.

New Testament texts in keeping with the ideas of the parable

Mt 5:36-37	Let your speech be "yes", "no". Simplicity, candour.
Mt 12:1-14	Do not absolutise custom, rites, traditions.
Mt 12:22-32	Don't be too sure. You may sin against the Holy Spirit.
Mt 22	Questions put to Jesus by Pharisees and teachers of the Law. They already knew the answers but wanted to catch Jesus out. Jesus replies forthrightly without dogmatism.
Mt 23:6-8	Do not want to be called "teachers of the Law".

Mt 23: 13-28	Jesus accuses the teachers of the Law.
Mt 24:36	Jesus acknowledges that he does not know.
Mk 7:1-13	People can be misguided and misled. Knowledge is subject to surface impressions and prejudices.
Lk 18:9-14	Jesus humiliates those who feel too sure of themselves.
Jn 3:1-21	Nicodemus is not at all sure of his teaching.
Jn 9:1-41	There is such a thing as "spiritual kindness".
Acts 17:16-32	Paul cannot convince the "educated" and "learned" by rational arguments.
1 Cor 2	Paul attacks the wisdom of the world
1 Cor 3	and knowledge based only on reason.
1 Cor 10:14-15	Keep away from "idol worship". All absolutes are idols.

11
The little fish

A happy little fish was swimming and frolicking near the bottom of the ocean. There he enjoyed the company of many friends. He could eat as much food as he wished and never seemed to lack for anything.

Then he began to swim upwards, higher and higher. He had never swum so high before.

"I wonder what it's like up there", he said to himself. "It seems to be growing much lighter and I can see things far more clearly than I could down there."

Before very long, the little fish reached the surface of the ocean. He was amazed to see how beautiful the sky looked and wondered what it must be like to go through the top of the water. He even managed, for a second, to push his head through the surface.

"How beautiful it looks! How exciting!" he gasped, seeing the edge of the sandy beach.

When he found himself once again beneath the waves, he felt despondent. Why should he have to go back down to that dark, gloomy life at the bottom of the ocean? It was so bright and warm outside. Why couldn't he go and live outside, where it was much brighter and warmer?

The little fish decided to jump out of the water as high as he could. He then felt the warmth of the sun even more. He could also see much further, beyond the beach and as far as some rows of trees, beautiful flowers and a street full of picturesque little bungalows.

He soon made up his mind to reach that shore and begin a new life. Nothing would now deter him, as he began swimming eagerly forwards until he eventually found himself washed up on the sand.

"Free at last", he cried. "I'm now ready to enjoy a wonderful new life, far away from that dull, cold life at the bottom of the water..."

Suddenly he felt a choking sensation. "Oh dear," he murmured, "I must have taken too much out of myself. I've tried to swim... too fast... too... quickly..."

He again tried to catch his breath but the choking feeling remained. A few minutes later, the little fish lay dead on the beach.

GENERAL SUGGESTIONS

Messages of the parable

- Happiness is what we are and where we are.
- Acceptance of our situation and the circumstances of our lives.
- The temptation of thinking that "the grass is greener on the other side".
- We are born for happiness and we are the ones who make or mar our happiness.
- Living out the implications of self-acceptance in our relations with others.

Ideas and applications of the parable

- God gives each a place in life, indicated by events, abilities and opportunities which can best bring joy and satisfaction.
- Happiness is not an abstraction. We will not find a non-personal state called "happiness" but only "happy people".
- We must accept ourselves and our circumstances not with *passive resignation* but with *positive and active* gladness and *thanksgiving*.
- Let us enjoy what we have and forget what we would *like* to have.
- A fish is happy being a fish, a bird a bird, a man a man, a woman a woman.
- For families, happiness is in the home, not in the glamorous world outside.
- For students, happiness is school or college, not political activism or drugs.
- For workers, happiness is in the place of work, not in the "gossip shop".
- For religious, happiness is in their communities, not in the social circuit.
- We are all bounded by limitations and constraints. By accepting these and operating within them, we shall find satisfaction.
- Life is given in bits and pieces. We must enjoy every present moment. Worry about the past or future will never bring enjoyment in the present.
- It is in the context of the present that happiness comes to us.
- God communicates his life, being, presence and his joy in the here-and-now. We have to find happiness and fulfilment *right at this moment.*
- By escaping the living present and taking refuge in the dead past or the unborn future, we run away from God, from ourselves, from joy. Let us not forget the momentous truth that happiness is what we are and *wherever we are.*

Bible texts in keeping with the ideas of the parable

Main texts:

Gen 3:1-24	Adam and Eve, not happy being human, wanted to become gods.
Mt 26:14-16	Judas searched for happiness in money,
Mt 26:47-50	outside the company of the Twelve.
Mt 27:3-5	The result: he hanged himself.
Lk 15:11-17	The prodigal son looked for happiness away from home. He ended up in the company of swine.
Lk 24:13-35	The disciples of Emmaus left their companions, expecting to find consolation outside their group. Their anxieties were not allayed until they met the Risen Lord.
Mt 6:25-34	Trust God. Do not worry about the future. Live in the present. Cast all your worries onto the Lord.

Other texts:

Mt 5:1-11	The Beatitudes: where true happiness lies.
Mt 6:16-21	True riches.
Mt 10:17-31	The rich young man missed his happiness by not doing what Jesus asked him to do. He missed his vocation in life.
Lk 2:21-52	Happiness in the Holy Family. Doing the will of God.
Lk 4:1-11	The devil tempted Jesus to seek happiness and fulfilment away from his Messianic vocation.
Lk 11:1-13	Place yourself in God's hands. He will see to your needs.
Lk 12:13-22	The rich fool wanted to find happiness in piling up riches.

Lk 18:15-17   To be like little children is indeed a source of joy.

Jn 21:20-22   Jesus and the other disciple. What Jesus tells Peter amounts to this: "What happens to the other is not your concern. You, follow me!"

12

The begging bowl

Chandrakant was an Indian beggar, who believed himself the lowest of the low. "I am no good for anything", he would often repeat to himself. "I am useless, a parasite. Nobody likes me and nobody will ever like me!"

The only thing he could really call his own was his filthy old begging bowl, which never left his side and which he constantly pushed in front of anyone he thought likely to give him money. Sometimes he did this shyly, acutely conscious of his own inadequacies. At other times, he thrust it boldly, almost vindictively, in front of some people, especially if he felt any jealousy towards them. He often felt this and therefore experienced satisfaction, rather than shame, in accepting charity.

He often walked into shops, asking shopkeeper and clients alike to give him alms. One day, after entering an old curio shop, he thrust the heavy old begging bowl under the shopkeeper's nose:

"Please, I beg you. Have pity on me. Just enough for a morsel of bread. I am hungry. Pity me!"

The shop-keeper simply stared at the dirty begging bowl. He finally took it from Chandrakant, saying,

"Let me have a closer look at that filthy bowl of yours."

"Please, sir," exclaimed Chandrakant, "let me have... It's the only..."

"Just a minute", interrupted the shopkeeper. "You're a funny sort of beggar. You're worth more than I am."

"Please, sir, do not mock me. I only wish to..."

"I'm serious. You're not a poor man. That huge old begging bowl of yours... Why don't you sell it? It's made of pure solid gold."

GENERAL SUGGESTIONS

Messages of the parable

- To improve your self-image.
- Most emotional and psychological problems stem from a poor self-image.
- Restoring "self-respect", "self-esteem", "self-confidence".
- Believe in your intrinsic worth; discover hidden strengths and talents.
- Tracing the growth and development of self-image.
- Discover and eradicate any "inferiority complex" or other "self-defeating" mechanisms operating on the psyche.

Ideas and applications of the parable

- The "real self" is one thing and the "imaginary self" is quite another.
- Our "imaginary self", posing as "self-image", conditions our thoughts, feelings and behaviour.
- Chandrakant perceived himself as a poor man but, in reality, he was rich. He therefore thought himself poor, felt poor and played the role of a beggar.
- It is practically impossible for us to perceive ourselves objectively and adequately. We perceive a minute part of ourselves, the tip of the iceberg.
- This explains our usually poor self-image, why we are more conscious of limitations than of strengths and talents.
- Personality and behavioural changes must begin in areas of "self-image". Without this basic change, all other changes remain superficial and short-lived.
- Improved perception of self makes us think better of ourselves. We shall then feel better and act more assertively.
- In childhood we knew ourselves through the perceptions of "significant people": parents and other relatives, teachers, friends, close associates.
- We saw ourselves reflected in their perceptions but human "mirrors" cannot be objective and accurate. They are coloured and conditioned by cultural values, assumptions and biases, as well as by their own personal deficiencies and complexes.
- Our images of childhood were therefore not accurate and yet, sadly, we interiorise them completely.
- This interiorised self-image rules our thinking, feelings and behaviour.
- We must re-evaluate and improve our self-image, in some of the following ways:
  • Implicit trust in ourselves.
  • Picking up courage and determination.
  • Searching for and discovering our strengths.
  • Accepting our uniqueness.

- Asserting ourselves – being "ourselves".
- Refusing to compare ourselves to others.
- Not evaluating or grading ourselves against outside standards.
- Loving ourselves.

– Helping others to discover their true selves by:
  - Accepting them unconditionally.
  - Not criticising them.
  - Being generous with our praise and appreciation of them.
  - Not involving them in invidious comparisons.
  - Trusting them implicitly.
  - Allowing them to be themselves.
  - Not putting them under our obligation.
  - Not making them feel they fall short of our expectations of them.

New Testament texts in keeping with the ideas of the parable

There are no specific texts in the New Testament on "self-image" but we see, in the Gospel as a whole, the manner in which Jesus dealt with all kinds of people. He was always reassuring and accepting in his dealings with them. In this way, Jesus changed people for the better. People discover their self-worth by the way they are treated.

Mt 5:21-22	Jesus wants us to treat others with great respect.
Mt 5:43-48	He even wants us to love our enemies.
Mt 7:1-5	He forbids us to judge others.
Mt 13:44-46	We can apply the parable of the hidden treasure and of the pearl to human beings.
Mt 4:18-22	Jesus chooses his disciples.
Lk 5:1-11	He sees worth
Mk 3:13-16	where others
Mk 9:9-13	saw none.

Lk 7:36-48	Jesus accepts and respects sinners, thus
Lk 19:1-10	transforming them: the sinful woman, Zacchaeus.
Jn 4:1-41	Adulterous women,
Jn 8:1-11	good thief, Peter, etc.
Mk 9:33-37	Jesus accepts and loves children, thus helping
Mk 10:13-16	them to grow.

13

Isaac

Isaac was the very poor father of a large family. Unable to provide food, he watched helplessly as, for the third successive night, his wife could give the children only a few crumbs before putting them to bed.

Soon in bed himself, he prayed earnestly: "God, have mercy on us. I entrust my family to your loving care. Please do not forget us."

That same night, Isaac had a dream in which a mysterious voice told him to leave his village and go into the big city. There, under a bridge, he would find a bag full of gold and his troubles would be over.

"Where? Under which bridge? How will it be hidden?" Isaac woke up still shouting these questions. He then realised he had been dreaming and lay still. Everyone else was asleep.

Yet the dream had been so vivid! He would have loved to believe it but thought this a waste of time. He tried to sleep again. Still the dream played on his mind and he remained wide awake. Why not go to the city, just exactly as the mysterious voice had said? After all, it was perhaps the answer to his prayer?

Although it was still very dark, Isaac began putting on his clothes. His wife then woke up and asked what he was doing. She found his answers ridiculous and told him he would be wasting his time. Undeterred, he set off for the city. He had nothing to lose by obeying his dream.

It was already mid-afternoon by the time his long, tiring journey ended. He quickly forgot his stiff legs and aching feet when, there in front of him, was the very bridge which he had seen in his dream! But where was the treasure hidden? He began carefully and surreptitiously to search underneath it. At regular instances, he cast furtive glances behind to see if anyone was watching.

"Hey, you there!" yelled a security guard from a nearby factory. "What do you think you're playing at?"

"Nothing", replied Isaac, somewhat startled.

"Nothing?! Don't give me 'nothing'. I've been watching you for the last ten minutes. You're looking for something to steal, aren't you?"

"No, honestly, I'm not", pleaded Isaac. "I was told in a dream to come here."

"A dream...", echoed the guard sarcastically. "So you believe in dreams, do you? Well, listen. I had a dream last night as well. I was told to go to a village, where I would find a bag full of gold buried behind the fireplace of a poor man called Isaac. You don't think I believed that, do you? So push off! Stop mooching about here and clear off back to where you belong!"

Excitedly Isaac returned home, running, trotting, walking much faster than he had come earlier in the day.

As soon as he rushed into his house, he began digging behind the fireplace. There, to everyone's amazement, was the bag of gold.

GENERAL SUGGESTIONS

Messages of the parable

- Fulfilment, peace and lasting happiness are not found outside but *within* us.
- To find these treasures, we go outside ourselves in strange and uncertain directions, only to return to ourselves and eventually find them deep inside.
- We journey outside in search of God, only to return inwards and finally discover him in the centre of our being.
- The need to grow in understanding of the profound words of Jesus: "The Kingdom of God is within you".

Ideas and applications of the parable

- We think ourselves poor and destitute when, in fact, we are rich with riches no thief can take and no moth can destroy.
- We think ourselves away from God, when God is more present than we are to ourselves.
- We search for truth, beauty, fulfilment and for God, wherever we can, but our primary instinct is to go outside ourselves.
- Unless we go outside ourselves with generosity and detachment, we shall never find ultimate meaning in life and never find God.
- Life is ultimately a journey homewards, inwards. Sooner or later, our outward search will turn us inwards.
- Any "spiritual journey" must finally turn inwards, into the recesses of our hearts.
- Any "spiritual odyssey" must lead to finding God in the deepest layers of our being.

- In Christ's "odyssey", he left heaven to touch earth, only to re-enter heaven in a glorious return.
- This dialectical movement forwards and backwards, giving up and entering into possession, is an essential part of human endeavour to transcend ourselves but then to return to ourselves in the divine immanence.
- Alienated from ourselves, we seek wholeness, meaning and fruition outside ourselves. Lost traces of ourselves, scattered outside, finally converge inwards towards the core of our being. By returning to ourselves, we integrate the alienated parts, becoming whole, one again with ourselves, with God and with the world.
- All the "treasures" (peace, joy, serenity, fulfilment, truth, love, beauty) which we frantically seek in external things (money, pleasures, success, fame, honour, status, power) are already in our hearts. Only by renouncing those external things will we finally enter the treasure- house of the heart.
- Great saints and mystics followed this path: renouncing fleeting things of the world and encountering God in the depths of their being.
- Despite transcendental human nature, our two-way journey would ultimately be into the void if Christ had not redeemed and transfigured our transcendence by divine transcendental immanence.
- Created things in the external world are good, partly in themselves but more for the greater good to which they point. They are signposts to where God meets us in the depths of his being and which we must read correctly if our journey is to be truly rewarding.

New Testament texts in keeping with the ideas of the parable

Mt 5:1-11	The Beatitudes: blessedness is found in detachment, out of oneself.
Mt 5:13-16	We are salt and light. We have not yet discovered what we are and what we are supposed to do in the world.

Mt 6:5-6	When you pray, do not go out of yourself. Close the door of your room – that is, of your heart. God is there.
Mt 6:16-21	True riches are found in our hearts.
Mt 10:37-39	To possess our lives, we have to lose them.
Mt 13:44-46	The hidden treasure and the pearl.
Mk 10:17-31	The rich young man searched for treasures outside his heart and missed Jesus.
Lk 12:13-21	The rich fool.
Lk 17:20-22	The Kingdom of God is within you.
Lk 24:13-35	Emmaus: the disciples went away from Jerusalem to find Jesus on the way and returned to Jerusalem.
Jn 3:5	To enter the Kingdom of God we have to be born again.

14

Can they not taste by themselves?

An international trading company asked an Indian producer to supply samples of mangoes which would include varieties of choice at different prices. These were accordingly prepared in five separate boxes, which the producer asked his workmen to label and with which he sent an accompanying letter to the trading company:

Dear Sirs,

In compliance with your request, I am forwarding five boxes containing 1 doz. mangoes each, selected and priced as follows:

Box No. 1: Alphonso Mangoes
  @ 10 rupees each ... ... Best quality
Box No. 2: Pires Mangoes
  @ 5 rupees each ... ... Second Best quality
Box No. 3: Fernandes Mangoes
  @ 5 rupees each ... ... Good quality
Box No. 4: Malgoba Mangoes
  @ 3 rupees each ... ... Cheap quality
Box No. 5: Langda Mangoes
  @ 1 rupee each   ... ... Cheapest quality

Awaiting your order and assuring you of our prompt and efficient service.

Yours faithfully,

....

Unfortunately the packers mixed up the labels, so that qualities and prices were incorrectly labelled. When the importers opened mangoes marked "Best quality Alphonso Mangoes", they really began tasting the cheapest quality Langda.

Undeterred, however, they pronounced these deliciously sweet, despite the high price, which they considered excellent value for such quality. They would definitely place a large order.

Tasting second best quality Pires, they believed themselves to be tasting cheap quality Malgoba. They grimaced at how sour those tasted but agreed that such inferiority was reflected in the much lower price.

When the importers finally opened the box marked "Langda... Cheapest quality", they decided not even to taste. After all, what could possibly be expected at only one rupee each! Little did they know that this box actually contained the best Alphonso mangoes, which they now threw on to a pile of rubbish.

Some crows, watching from a distance, were soon delightedly down on the best mangoes and enjoyed a feast:

"How stupid human beings are", said one of the crows. "Can't they taste for themselves the quality of the mangoes, instead of having to rely on the labels?"

"Those people pride themselves", said another crow, "on their rationality but we, being irrational, just taste and see!"

"We trust our experience", added a third. "We don't need labels and titles to know where good mangoes are. We can judge by ourselves where sweetness, worth and quality lie."

GENERAL SUGGESTIONS

Messages of the parable

- The reliability of our perceptions.
- Evaluating things, events and persons by using our faculties of reason, experience, senses and intuition.
- The *focus* of our mind must move from the outside world and what others say to our own inner world and what we ourselves feel and think.
- A need to resist the craze people have for credentials, degrees, diplomas, titles and honours.

Ideas and applications of the parable

- Today a high premium is placed on external trappings of power or authority.
- Human worth is within, in what we are, not in what we are thought to be or show ourselves to be.
- The value of things must be judged in themselves, not by reference to the persons who owned or originated the things.
- Labels, titles, degrees, etc. are props to bolster our poor self-image.
- We shelter behind them to shield ourselves from criticism and rejection.
- The more insecure people are, the more they cling to labels and laurels.

- We prefer make-believe to reality, appearances and showmanship to truth.
- Many feel it is not important to be but to appear good, honest, respectable, capable, etc. There is a cheap glamour in people who make us feel good, honest, etc., although we may not really be so.
- Titles and honorific labels are "status symbols". Those who cannot earn them try to buy them. Titles and honours often become ritualised. A person's real status may be replaced by a semblance of it whenever a titular status is conferred: no sooner does a dishonest person acquire a title than he is invested with respectability. Many political leaders were once common criminals but have suddenly become honourable, acquiring world-wide respectability.
- A clever man is considered ignorant if he has no degree after his name.
- Judgements are made according to worldly values: money, popularity, pomp, fame, status, commercial values. Their real worth is not considered but only what is summarily accepted by the world.
- We are afraid to be different: to think, feel or speak differently. We like to play safe and feel at one with other people.
- We are afraid to stand by our values, convictions and perceptions.
- Before venturing an opinion, we want to know what others feel, so that we can think and feel likewise. With no will of our own, our willing is done for us by the latest fad, fashion or fancy.
- Animals trust their perceptions, knowing what is good and bad for them, what tastes good or bad. Human beings do not trust their perceptions.
- For most of us, what is beautiful is not that which arouses our aesthetic sensibility but that which advertising and the media make beautiful.
- Slaves to prevailing tastes and fashions of our consumer society, we fall prey to open or hidden persuasions from advertisers or political demagogues.

– Trading our uniqueness for a mess of potage, we have lost our mind, judgement, discretion and soul.

New Testament texts in keeping with the ideas of the parable

Mt 5:33-37	Be honest and direct in your speech.
Mt 6:1-6	Do your religious duties without advertising them. God looks at the heart, not at the appearances.
Mt 7:15-20	You will know a tree by its fruit. Judge
Mt 12:33-35	people by their intrinsic worth and the value of their deeds.
Mt 7:21-23	"Not anyone who calls me 'Lord, Lord...' but the one who..."
Mt 21:23-27	The Jews wanted titles and credentials: "On whose authority do you do all this?"
Mt 23:1-12	Jesus tells us not to aspire to any titles or to be called "Teacher..., Master..., Father..."
Mt 23:13-28	Jesus detests all hypocrisy and appearances.
Mk 7:1-13	Do not stick to external rules and show.
Mk 7: 14-23	A person's heart is what counts. True worth is inside.
Mk 9:33-36	Who is the greatest?
Lk 4:16-30	Jesus is rejected in Nazareth. He had no titles or credentials. No prophet is accepted in his own land.
Lk 6:45	Good things come from a good person's heart.
Lk 7:18-23	Jesus shows his "credentials" to John the Baptist's disciples: deeds, actions, not titles and labels.
Lk 12:13-21	The rich fool: a man's true worth does not come from what he owns but from what he is.
Lk 18:9-14	Pharisee and tax collector: who is acceptable in God's eyes? Why?

87

Lk 21:1-4	The widow's mite. It is not what one gives but the attitude of the giver which counts before God.
Jas 2:1-4	Do not judge by appearances.
Jas 2:14-24	Faith in action.

15

Autobiography of a coconut

I was born on top of a sturdy tree, which grew in sandy soil along the coastal strip. From my perch I had a fantastic view of everything around me.

I was very happy and proud to be a coconut. I used to think my father was marvellous until, one day, I heard some passers-by cursing him and the whole family. If I remember rightly, one of them said:

"It's so hot today! If only this d—d coconut tree could give us some shade. I hate coconuts. So rough, so ugly and shapeless. No leaves, no flowers, no scent even."

This made me feel so miserable that something seemed to change within me. How could I not have seen it all before? I really was ugly, deformed almost. I felt ashamed and decided that no one would ever be allowed to see the ugliness within me...

I began building around myself a very thick, hard and resistant shell to protect my inside from view. After all, there was obviously nothing good inside me. If anyone ever saw inside me, I would become even more despised and rejected. I therefore spun around myself a layer of rough brown hairy stuff, unpleasant to the touch, so that nobody would dare touch me. I hated to be touched or patted.

After a number of weeks, spent gloomily brooding over my unhappiness and hardly ever talking to my brothers and sisters, I was suddenly surprised by a violent storm. We were all tossed around and I clung, terrified, to my father, afraid of being hurled from the tree.

But all was in vain. I lost my grip and felt myself being hurled downwards, falling into black emptiness. I found myself lying dazed on the ground, bruised and suffering from concussion. Alone and trembling with fear, I thought the only thing left was to wait for death.

My end had surely come when a group of those hateful passers-by approached me...

Yet how surprised and delighted I was to hear one of them remark:

"Look! What a lovely coconut! That certainly is a bit of luck."

AUTOBIOGRAPHY OF A COCONUT

Hardly able to believe my ears, I felt myself being lifted up and shaken next to the ear of a young boy. Then his nose smelt me and his mouth spoke directly to me:

"What a fresh, sweet, tasty coconut you must be! I'm certainly glad I found you."

What? Me? Fresh? Sweet? There must have been some mistake. Surely I was only a dull, shapeless, ugly and tasteless thing, content just to be left alone.

90

The young boy began carefully to remove the rough brown hairs which I had grown around myself as protection. He did so gently, as if wishing not to harm me. For the first time in months I felt happy again until, without warning, the young boy picked up a large stone and began to hit me hard. With ever-increasing speed and force, he struck me again and again. Yelling with pain, I wanted to ask him what he was looking for and beg him to stop. Surely he must realise that, inside me, there was nothing but ugliness. What could he possibly be trying to find underneath my hard shell?

A few seconds later, there was a loud crack and I felt myself splitting open. Some juice began oozing through my wounds and, to my amazement, the boy and his friends tried to drink it. From their gasps of delight, I could tell they were enjoying it. They remarked how sweet and cool it was.

My greatest surprise finally came when, after breaking away parts of my shell, they tore away some of my insides. It was spotless white! My insides looked beautiful and were obviously enjoyable to eat.

"People like me!" I exclaimed. "I'm not ugly and useless. Please, please, eat me. Eat all of me! I'm so glad to give pleasure to people who have finally made me believe in myself."

GENERAL SUGGESTIONS

Messages of the parable

- Discovering our inner riches.
- Growth in self-esteem.
- Why we have a poor image of ourselves.
- Discovering the "self-defeating mechanisms" used to cover parts of ourselves which we do not like and which we reject.
- Improving our self-image.

91

Ideas and applications of the parable

- Everyone is like the coconut: hidden treasures beneath a harsh exterior.
- Mistrusting their inner riches, people harden their outer appearance to protect a poor self-image.
- God made everyone unique, beautiful and precious. We are wrong to make people feel inadequate according merely to society's arbitrary standards. No children are ever born with an "inferiority complex" but we impose this on them.
- The opinions of others about us influence us more than we think of ourselves.
- We are not "actors" and do not "act". We are rather "reactors" who "react". We let ourselves be shaped by others, by society, by external influences.
- Unless others believe in us, we will not believe in ourselves.
- Fear of being rejected by others leads to self-rejection.
- Only from the outside may be activated a process of improving our self-image. Someone has to believe in us for us to believe in ourselves.
- Our "ugliness" is a false front intended to keep others at arm's length.
- Fear of being hurt makes us build walls which are not part of us and which can be broken down.
- If we reject ourselves, how can we expect others to accept us?
- What hurts most is not rejection by others but the fear that their rejection "confirms" our unworthiness.
- Do not take to heart disparaging remarks. If people like us, well and good; if they do not, all the worse for them!
- Our best gift to others is "unconditional" acceptance of them.
- Trust, respect and admiration for others will overcome their poor self-image.
- We must speak cautiously about the young, the weak, the poor and the insecure. Indiscretions could lead to their withdrawal and even self-hatred.

New Testament texts in keeping with the ideas of the parable

It is not easy to find texts in the New Testament bearing directly on the topics of "self-image" and "defence mechanisms" but the Gospels show how Jesus dealt with the poor and despised. He always accepted them and showed unshakeable trust in them:

Mt 4:18-22 Mt 10:1-4	Choosing his disciples from the poor and uneducated.
Mt 5:21-22	He condemns "name-calling", abuse and insults.
Mt 7:1-1	He forbids us to judge anyone.
Mt 18:1-4	Who is the greatest? Where is true worth found?
Mk 7:14-23	The human heart is what counts, not the appearances.
Mk 10:13-16	Jesus blesses children, takes them seriously, thus enhancing their self-image.
Mk 2:13-14	He calls Matthew, the tax-collector. He believes in him.
Mk 6:1-4	Jesus is rejected in Nazareth. His fellow-townspeople could not accept his worth, judging him by externals.
Mk 12:41-44	Jesus praises the poor widow. He reads her heart.
Lk 2:6-19	The first recipients of the Good News: poor and lowly shepherds.
Lk 7:36-50	Jesus accepts and praises the sinful woman, changing her life for good.
Lk 8:19-21	Jesus's mother and brothers: no other relationships count for him, other than a devoted and loving heart.
Lk 15:11-32	The parable of the prodigal son shows goodness in an apparently rotten heart.
Lk 18:9-14	The Pharisee and the tax collector. Who is the better?
Lk 19:1-10	Gold is found in a rapacious tax collector's heart.

Lk 23:39-43	Trust a thief and change his heart: the Good Thief.
Jn 1:45-48	Jesus discovers goodness in a cynic's heart: Nathanael.
Jn 8:1-11	By showing concern, Jesus changes the adulterous woman's heart.
Jn 9:1-41	The blind man learns wisdom and courage.
Jn 21:15-19	Jesus accepts Peter after his denial.

94

16

What's the trouble, Mr Toiler?

Mr Toiler was very hard-working and ambitious. Proud of his wealth and possessions, his driving ambition was eventually to fill his warehouse to capacity. Only when it was full to the brim with sacks of grain, tins of sugar, drums of oil, tins and boxes of food, would he be truly satisfied. Each day he kept willing himself to work even harder:

"I'll soon have my warehouse full if only I can work harder each day and never slacken the pace."

At last, the great day arrived. Mr Toiler found it absolutely impossible to fit anything else into his warehouse. He even found it difficult to close the warehouse door!

Looking forward to a well-earned retirement, he nevertheless spent a restless night, waiting eagerly to inspect his warehouse again in the morning. He therefore found it easy to rise even earlier than usual and hurry out of his house.

On reaching the warehouse door, he fumbled excitedly with his key in the lock and finally flung open the door. To his horror, he found his warehouse half-empty.

"What's happened to my stock?" wailed Mr Toiler. "Thieves must have broken in during the night and stolen half of my supplies!"

Angrily he began to search through everything that remained, checking against his original list to discover what was missing. Yet everything seemed to be there! He failed to identify even one single item as having disappeared. How could the warehouse be only half-full if all his goods were still there?

"Well, there's nothing to be done", he concluded, "except more hard work, until my warehouse is filled to overflowing again."

For many more months Mr Toiler continued to work even harder than before until the warehouse doors could only just be shut again. After another restless night, he hurried back for a triumphant inspection but, to his even greater horror than on the first occasion, half the supplies seemed to be missing!

Once more he itemised everything which remained and compared this list with his original. Strange to relate, all seemed still intact and thieves could certainly not be suspected.

Nothing was to be done but more hard work and Mr Toiler succeeded, for the third time, to fill his warehouse. But, for the third time, he found it again only half-full

the next morning. Little did Mr Toiler realise that his wealth was not diminishing but that his warehouse was expanding, always leaving room for more stock.

GENERAL SUGGESTIONS

Messages of the parable

- The need to guard against a wrong system of values.
- The futility of a vaunting ambition to acquire more material possessions.
- Dangers of an exclusive concern with material prosperity, the stranglehold of consumerism and the illusion that progress must be inevitable.
- Advantages in a life of moderation; remaining content with what we have, instead of hankering for more.

Ideas and applications of the parable

- Mr Toiler's problem was not with his goods, of which he had sufficient for a life of leisure, but with a warehouse growing in proportion to its contents.
- The warehouse represents the human heart, storehouse of desire. The more we have, the more we want – greed growing in proportion to wealth and never satisfied.
- Mr Toiler symbolises a modern obsession to acquire more goods and to derive greater satisfaction from life.
- The vain hope of one day reaching the pinnacle of happiness and complete satisfaction, acquiring wealth beyond the dreams of avarice.
- This utopian myth is constantly nourished by slogans to "Produce more!", "Consume more!", "Live life to the full!", "Never give up!"
- Whenever the "rat-race" becomes a struggle for survival, frustration and disenchantment are inevitable results.

- The ceaseless urge to feed the insatiable monster of production must be replaced by the satisfaction of living more human lives.
- Is the true purpose of life "to have" or "to be", "to own" or "to enjoy"?
- When we savour the good things of life with a miser's greed, they become Dead Sea fruit on our lips.

Bible texts in keeping with the ideas of the parable

Prov 28:6-11	"Better the poor contented than the rich."
Prov 30:8-9	"Give me neither poverty nor riches."
Eccles 2:8-11	"Vanity
Eccles 4:7-8	of vanities!
Eccles 5:12-1	All is vanity."
Mt 5:1-11	The Beatitudes: "Blessed are the poor in spirit..."
Mt 6:11	Give us "our daily bread". This is enough.
Mt 6:19-21	Riches in heaven: true riches neither robbed nor rusted.
Mt 6:24-34	God and possessions: truth is God's providence.
Mt 26:14-16	Judas betrays Jesus.
Mk 10:17-27	The rich young man.
Mk 10:28-31	Get 100% out of "your riches".
Lk 6:20-27	Where true happiness and sorrow lie.
Lk 12:13-21	The rich fool filled his warehouse but never enjoyed it.
Lk 16:14-15	The teachers of the Law make fun of Jesus because he was not in love with money.
Lk 16:19-31	The rich man and Lazarus.
Jn 12:4-6	He loves money.
1 Tim 6:6-10	"We brought nothing into the world. Desire for money is the root of all evil."
1 Tim 6:17-19	"Command the rich not to be proud."
Jas 1:9-11	Poverty and riches.
Jas 5:1-3	Warning to the rich.
Rev 3:17-19	"You say I am rich..."

17

Thou shalt not have other gods before me!

In such a scientific age as ours, it is not unusual to find a family worshipping "science" as its presiding deity. The Prestige family was a prime example.

Mr Prestige insisted that both children, Norbert and Tamara, should become doctors. Mrs Prestige agreed, believing that only by becoming doctors or engineers could today's children hope to enjoy a high standard of living.

Imagine how surprised his parents were when Norbert asked for a guitar as a birthday present:

"I love music and my teachers say that I should try to develop my natural talents further."

"A guitar?!" exclaimed a startled Mr Prestige. "You'll get no such thing. Remember, you're in your final year at school and you've got to work hard at your exams to qualify for medical college. You can't afford distractions like guitars or any other kind of musical instrument!"

With Norbert's musical talents sacrificed on the altar of "science", Tamara's love of literature soon met the same fate:

"I'd love to be a writer and my English teacher says I should study for a B.A. Honours, with English as the main subject. I'll need to enrol for English next year in Form Six."

"What! English?!! Certainly not. You just keep concentrating on maths and science. We haven't spent all this money on you just to see it frittered away on literature courses!"

Although both children continued, during the next few years, to ask their parents for various other favours – to join a cricket club, to enrol in art classes, to attend youth clubs, to take dancing lessons—Mr and Mrs Prestige firmly refused each request. Any form of voluntary service was especially condemned and neither Norbert nor Tamara had any hope of devoting time to the Young Vincentians, *CAFOD, YCW* or others:

"Schools and universities aren't put there to feed the hungry or help the down-and-outs! Just you concentrate on your studies. That's what we've made sacrifices for, so show us a bit of gratitude, for a change, by passing all your exams."

And pass their exams they certainly did. Social life, personal friendships, love, artistic talents – all had been duly sacrificed but Norbert and Tamara eventually made the grade. Norbert became an aeronautical engineer and Tamara a neurologist.

A bright future now awaited them and there were really only very few drawbacks: both young people had become heartless, friendless and selfish characters. They were mindless, loveless and joyless automatons but Mr and Mrs Prestige were nevertheless proud of their two children, to whom they had given the brightest future and ensured a high standard of living.

GENERAL SUGGESTIONS

Messages of the parable

- Questionable values by which we run our homes, institutions, schools, colleges, even our churches.
- Youths should be encouraged to take their own decisions and follow their consciences.
- Manipulation in our society: in choosing their vocation or changing direction in life, people are constantly forced into our Procrustean beds of behaving, complying with ideologies, traditions, group interest or maintaining the status quo. A hidden imperialism forces them to do what others want.
- Material satisfactions concentrate on easy access to wealth and power. Instead of making life more human and satisfying, they actually impoverish it, killing what is best in us.
- True joy and fulfilment come from using God-given talents, not in suppressing them for the sake of inherited structures and vested interests.

Ideas and applications of the parable

- Like so many other parents who slavishly conform to prevalent social values, the Prestiges crushed all that was best in their children.
- Their own worldly values – money, prestige, status, success – were mistakenly lumped together under what they called a "high standard of living".
- They brainwashed their children into accepting and living by these values.
- Money and prestige were not as good for their children as friendship, social concern, art, music, literature, love of the poor. The simple and unspoilt natures of Norbert and Tamara told them that.
- By conforming to their parents' wishes, they ruined their lives. They achieved all their parents wanted for them but they did not acquire happiness or a sense of fulfilment.

101

- Are we, as parents, teachers, pastors, ruining the lives of those in our charge?
- We must teach them to challenge hedonistic and materialistic values.
- No parent, teacher or minister has a right to impose views on their charges.
- Happiness and fulfilment will not come to children if we smother what is best in them or force them to conform to a predetermined social mould and stifle any possible dissent.
- They will feel immense self-satisfaction if left free to be themselves and to become what they are best suited to be according to their own convictions.
- High "standard of living" is really life-diminishing and is not the same as high "quality of life" which is life-enhancing. When Norbert and Tamara had secured a high "standard of living", the stench of rottenness had already begun to foul their "quality of life".
- Science, or rather "scientism", has become a mighty idol on whose altar children have been sacrificed. This is generated and, in turn, generates the molochs of prestige, status and money, which devour the soul.
- An education system imbued with these wrong values will drive pupils to personal frustration and moral failure.
- Schools and colleges of such a system would not "form" but only "inform". They would not "educate" for life but only "train" for a living. Products of schools and colleges should be fully humanised young people, prepared for the serious business of life. Too often they have been taught to be ambitious and only capable of meeting the demands of a competitive society.
- A college prospectus may profess one set of values which includes love, co-operation, social concern, patriotism, humanitarianism, honesty and integrity. Yet, in real life, we practise exactly the opposite: competitiveness, selfishness, individualism, prestige, status, money.

– There is a "hidden agenda" in all we do and teach. We must remember that "values are caught, not taught". Students catch the values we practise and do not learn the values we teach.

Bible texts in keeping with the ideas of the parable

Idolatry attributes prerogatives to something which is not God:

- Seeing in it an "absolute meaning".
- Making it the be-all and end-all.
- Sacrificing to it all we have and all we are.

Old Testament texts on money and idol-worship

Lev 26:1	"I am the Lord your God..."
Wis 12:23-25	"You have tormented them... for they went astray..."
Wis 14:12-31	The madness of idol-worship.
Ps 113:4-8	Their idols are silver and gold.
Is 46:6-9	They squander their gold to fashion a god.

New Testament texts on prestige and money

Mt 5:1-11	The Beatitudes: values of Christ.
Mt 6:19-21	Riches in heaven.
Mt 6:24	You cannot serve two masters – God and money.
Mt 13:53-58	Jesus was rejected in Nazareth for being the son of a carpenter, not for being the son of a doctor or engineer!
Mt 23:1-2	Jesus condemns the teachers of the Law who wanted titles, prestige and status.
Mt 25:31-46	True greatness before God is counted by how much we love, not by how much we own.
Mk 9:32-37	Who is the greatest?
Mk 10:17-31	The rich young man misses true joy because of his wealth.

103

Mk 10:35-45	James' and John's request: they wanted power and influence but were promised sufferings.
Lk 4:1-13	Jesus overcame the temptation of becoming rich and powerful.
Lk 12:13-21	The rich fool: a man's worth is not made up of what he owns.
Lk 14:7-14	First places at the wedding feast. The first will be last and the last first.
Lk 22:24-27	Argument of greatness and prestige.
1 Tim 6:6-10	Love of money is a source of all kinds of evil.
Jas 1:9-11	Poverty and riches.
Jas 5:1-6	Warning to the rich.

18
Margaret

Margaret was a young, enthusiastic and very popular teacher. Her pupils loved her and their parents thought the world of her. She was liked and respected by her colleagues, admired by her superiors and by the school governors.

She loved to be with the children, to talk with them and join in their games during recreation times. Everyone, including her pupils, called her by her Christian name.

When the Headmistress was due to retire, many other members of staff, governors and parents asked Margaret if she would apply for the vacancy. She had really never set her sights on a headship but was eventually persuaded to fill in the application forms. After being short-listed and interviewed, she was duly appointed the new Headmistress.

The congratulations which followed made Margaret truly happy in her new position but she also wondered if, somewhat isolated in her office, she might miss the closer contact with children whom she used to see every day in the class-room.

Soon, however, the children were happy to show the same friendship towards her and, during each recreation, there were always throngs of them pushing through her door. They delighted in calling at her office to talk with her and invite her to continue in their games. Still everyone simply addressed her as "Margaret".

Often children would be late arriving back in their class room after recreation, so great had been the congestion in the new Headmistress's office. This worried her and she decided to adopt a stricter approach. From then onwards, the pupils must queue in an orderly fashion outside her door and not try to push in all at once. She also told them to address her as "Headmistress", instead of the rather too familiar "Margaret".

Although more orderly queues began to form, no one seemed to pay any attention to Margaret's request about being addressed as "Headmistress". Everyone continued to use her Christian name. This really began to annoy her.

She decided to have printed a big notice, with the word HEADMISTRESS printed boldly across it and placed in front of her on the desk. Yet still adults and children insisted on calling her "Margaret".

Although fewer children were seeking her attention during recreation times, her annoyance was increasing over their familiar form of address. She therefore had printed a much bigger notice, which nobody could possibly avoid seeing:

HEADMISTRESS

She placed this immediately in front of herself, pointing to it and insisting that she must be called "Headmistress".

Unfortunately, no one seemed to pay attention to the notice, nor even to bother addressing the Headmistress by any name at all. The notice was so huge that the children could not see above it. Any child coming into Margaret's room honestly believed that there was no one there and immediately went out again.

Some of the more faithful ones returned on a few more occasions but finally grew tired of finding the room apparently empty. Margaret therefore remained there all alone, at last respected by everyone but friendless, sad, lonely and forgotten.

GENERAL SUGGESTIONS

Messages of the parable

- The *concept, purpose* and *function* of obedience and authority.
- Authority exercised according to the human dignity of both whoever exercises it and whoever is subject to it.
- Distinction between authority of service and authority of power.
- Distinction between personal and formal authority.
- Psychological blocks preventing proper functioning of authority.

Ideas and applications of the parable

- As an ordinary teacher, Margaret was popular, influential, much loved and enjoying whatever authority she held.
- As a headmistress, she lost the authority enjoyed as a class-room teacher and therefore lost the rapport enjoyed with everyone in the school.
- Margaret ceased to be herself, the loving and loveable person she was, and began hiding behind her role of headmistress.
- There are two kinds of authority: *formal* and *personal*.

107

Margaret originally enjoyed personal authority and was loved, trusted, obeyed and respected.

- As headmistress, she was given formal authority, which slowly asserted itself over her personal authority. She ceased to be the object of love and instead became an object of reverential awe.
- Both kinds of authority are necessary to a good boss.
- Personal authority is earned and, unlike formal authority, is not a creation of the law.
- Jesus never had formal authority among Jewish rulers. That is why Pharisees and teachers of the Law asked him, "On whose authority do you do these things?" Yet Jesus wielded great personal authority and spoke as one having authority.
- The Pharisees cared only for formal authority. In the corridors of authority, Christ was personalistic, the Pharisees legalistic.
- Formal authority divides people into superiors and inferiors, tending to make superiors tyrants and inferiors slaves.
- Personal authority turns those subject into friends, co-operators and partners. Those in authority are turned into fathers, facilitators, guides and animators.
- Formal authority makes obedience burdensome, humiliating, hurtful and distasteful. Personal authority makes it pleasant, enriching and liberating.
- Formal authority isolates. The rank-and-file feel segregated and unwanted, separated from the elite.
- Personal authority makes authorities and subjects all feel understood, accepted and loved. Personal authority builds community spirit.
- Formal authority holds people together by legal, conventional, artificial bonds, uniting strangers to one another through expediency, not solidarity.
- Authority is meant to help, guide and orientate the community towards a togetherness which is kind, co-operative and responsible.
- Authority must never crush people, to exploit or to suppress individual freedom, enforcing compliance,

docility or passivity by a kind of social or cultural colonialism.

- Superiors should not satisfy their own needs and aspirations so much as those of their subordinates.
- People in authority have been given a "trust", a "commission" to serve the community. This is not a "privilege" but an obligatory burden imposed in the interests of society.
- Authority flows from our social nature. As a necessity, it remains unpleasant, a "necessary evil". It will always be needed to regulate and co-ordinate levels of existence in society but it curtails personal freedom, that most precious of birth-rights.
- Before God, there are really neither superiors nor inferiors. While, metaphysically, all are equal, the world of human relationships nevertheless assigns various roles according to the needs of the common good.
- Superiors should not be too conscious of their formal authority and not call attention to it explicitly when they have occasion to use it.
- Honours, fame, money, benefits, privilege, protocol and preference should not follow upon the exercise of true authority. If those in authority demand these things, they lose their credibility with anyone having a right to both love and protection from them. Their *personal* authority is lost in the process, being replaced by formal authority and all that this entails: force, repression, sanctions, punishments, warnings...
- Superiors should be loved, not feared.
- Obedience is one thing, servility quite another.
- Obedience should dignify, not degrade.
- The term "crisis of obedience" is really a "crisis of authority". If authority is rightly conceived and properly exercised, obedience will lose its critical stance.
- Authority and obedience complement each other. The problem is not with one or the other but rather with them both in their inter-relationships.

109

New Testament texts in keeping with the ideas of the parable

Mt 2:16-18	Killing of the innocent children. Abuse of authority.
Mt 7:28-29	Jesus taught with "authority".
Mt 13:53-58	Jesus rejected by his own people in Nazareth. He had no formal authority.
Mt 18:1-5	Who is the greatest?
Mt 20:20-28	Mother's request. True greatness and authority.
Mt 23:1-12	Warning against those who want formal authority and titles.
Mt 23:13-28	Jesus condemns the hypocrisy of those in authority.
Mk 11:27-33	On whose authority?
Lk 3:1-20	John the Baptist's personal authority.
Lk 14:7-11	First places at the banquet table.
Lk 22:24-27	The argument of greatness.
Jn 13:1-17	Washing of the feet.
Jn 19:8-11	Jesus and Pilate. "I have authority..." (Abuse of authority).

19

Listen to the greyhounds

The race had just ended. With their tongues hanging frothily from their mouths, panting, their coats steaming with sweat, the greyhounds trotted exhaustedly back to their kennels.

Once again they had all done their very best to catch that elusive hare but none had succeeded:

"We'll just have to keep trying harder next time", vowed Silver Princess, a sleek, light grey, almost white-looking animal and the only bitch in the race.

"It's all right you saying that, my dear", observed Daniel's Den, one of the older dogs, his dark flanks heaving under the strain. "We try so hard every time but never seem to get any nearer to that b— hare!"

"We'll get there, in the end", murmured a few of the others. "Practice will pay off, you'll see."

None of them realised, of course, that they were talking about an artificial hare, driven by an electric motor and controlled mechanically to keep just ahead of the chasing greyhounds.

"The faster we run, the faster the flaming hare seems to run", was the nearest to the truth any of the poor dogs ever came. After every race, their conversation combined both disappointment at failure and determination to succeed eventually in catching their prey. They were all sure that at last one of them would succeed very soon.

Anyone listening to such naive conversations would indeed feel sorry for those poor animals, so honest in their endeavours but so gullible and easily deluded. Yet, not very far from them, sitting in the grandstand, could be heard the remarkably similar conversations of their human superiors:

"I slogged like mad to win that big contract last week. It would have brought in a tidy sum... I nearly made it,

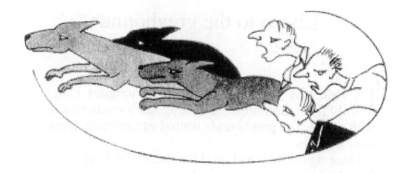

as well. But it just slipped through my hands. Still, next time, I'll be a bit smarter and we'll get there in the end."

"Yes, I know what you mean", came a reply. "I may not be in your line of business but I certainly know what disappointment is."

"You? Disappointed?" interrupted the first voice. "But you're a consultant and one of the country's top surgeons."

"Maybe I am, but I still don't want to stay in the same job all my life. No, if I worked hard enough, knew the right people a little better and had a bit of luck, I could end up as Surgeon General."

"I just missed being elected by less than a thousand votes", interjected a third voice, "so I know what disappointment is. I'd worked my socks off running all over the constituency but, next time, I'll cover even more ground and really concentrate on the issues that'll win votes. I'm bound to get there in the end."

"I'm glad to hear you all talking like that", added a fourth voice, "I never stop telling the children to work harder at school. They don't seem to realise that success only comes if you put the effort into it. Too many people in the world today fail to realise that success is only a matter of working that little bit harder."

We might well wonder what the poor greyhounds would have thought if they had been able to overhear what some of the spectators were saying.

Messages of the parable

-   Human life is *qualitative* not *quantitative*. For a responsible and committed person, living is a matter of *being* and not of *having*.
-   The futility of a modern life-style programmed for *running* without ever *stopping*, for *"becoming"* without ever eventually *"being"*.
-   "Success", as the world understands it, is totally different from *"successful living"*. The "success" philosophy implies an endless chase for the satisfaction of material wants, at the cost of improvement in the quality of life.
-   The biblical warning that "a man's true life is not made up of the things he owns, no matter how rich he may be" (Lk 12:15).
-   People who pursue wealth, power and prestige must learn to begin living and enjoy what they have.

Ideas and applications of the parable

-   Our economy, education system, recreational activities, even our religious practices are tainted with the cult of "success".
-   Our culture has identified "success" with market-place epithets: *more, bigger, faster, higher!*
-   To succeed, we have to *have* more, *acquire* more, have *more fun*, *know more*, climb *higher*, *reach* the top!
-   The race is endless, the pace always accelerating. Only the running matters.
-   Success will always elude us because we are running after a shadow, a mirage.
-   Condemned to failure, to perpetual frustration, we are no better than dumb greyhounds running after the illusory hare.
-   We have been conditioned to believe that success means wealth, power, popularity, applause, status,

getting to the top of the heap, outstripping our rivals, mowing down our opponents.

- Whereas true success lies in contentment, acceptance, patience, availability, trust, peace, joy and hope in a definitive future.
- Our idea of success makes it impossible to achieve. Only one person can reach the top, only one become "successful". Yet this will be in only one area of life and not necessarily in others. An immensely successful businessman may be lacking in certain fields of knowledge or may be deficient in leadership. He too will therefore still feel frustrated.
- Many die without having lived. The whole of their lives has been a slow living death if they refused to stop grabbing. We must enjoy what we have, refrain from "possessing" and start "being".
- Success does not depend on trying ever harder, straining every nerve to carve a bigger niche in life but thereby killing peace and joy and banishing truly successful living.
- Human beings are not made for mere work, for brutish and feverish activity without end. On the contrary, work and activity are there at our behest, for our enjoyment.
- Many years have been spent sacrificing everything to the "moloch of success" but it is now time to worship the true God of peace, serenity, quiet, fruition and joy.
- We must aspire not to *have more* but to *live more*, not to *acquire more* but to *enjoy more*.

New Testament texts in keeping with the ideas of the parable

Mt 5 :1-11	The Beatitudes: true satisfaction and fruition.
Mt 6:19-21	Riches in heaven: strive after them.
Mt 6:24-34	God and possessions. Do not fret unduly.

Mt 23:1-12	Do not try to be superior to others. Do not ask for titles: Master, Father, Leader.
Mk 9:33-37	Who is the greatest in the Kingdom of Heaven?
Mk 10:17-27	The rich young man: he was not free but a slave to wealth.
Mk 10:28-31	How to achieve your 100%.
Mk 10:35-45	James and John wanted to be more than the other disciples.
Mk 12:38-40	Jesus warns his hearers against the teachers of the Law who wanted to be considered better than anyone else.
Lk 4:1-13	Jesus is tempted by the devil to have pleasures, wealth and power.
Lk 11:43	Threats to the Pharisees. They wanted to have the best places and honours.
Lk 12:13-21	The rich fool.
Lk 14:7-11	"The first will be last and the last first."
Lk 15:1-3	The Pharisees object to Jesus entertaining sinners and outcasts. Yet such people were more honourable.
Jn 13:1-17	Washing of the feet. True greatness. Greatest success.
Jas 4:1-6	Friendship with the world.
Jas 5:1-3	Warnings to the rich.

20

A monkey business

Mr Robinson came home tired and weary, carrying a big monkey sitting comfortably on his back. Mrs Robinson was very worried to see her husband in such a state:

"What's wrong, darling?" she enquired sympathetically. "Why are you looking so tired and depressed?"

"To tell you the truth", he replied, "your mother's to blame as much as anybody. I've just called to see her and she started on at me all over again. Her and the rest of them. Your Jack and Doreen are nearly as bad. The whole lot of them are never off my back. They say you should never have married me. Your mother said she and your dad could see what would happen…"

"Nonsense, dear", interrupted his wife reassuringly. "You're the best husband in the world. Take no notice of them. I'll have a word with everybody the next time I go round. I'll sort it all out, don't you worry. You just sit down here and relax. Here, let me take that big monkey off your back."

She immediately took hold of the monkey and placed it on her own back. This made Mr Robinson feel most relieved. Relaxed and happy once more, he decided to meet some of his friends at the bowls club and go with them to the pub.

Not long after he had left, young Frank came home from school. He had a little monkey perched on his back.

"Oh, dear!" exclaimed his mother anxiously. "What's been happening at school today?"

"I'm just fed up, mum. The teacher blamed me for something I didn't do. She said I was cheeky and sly and a bad influence on the whole class."

"How dare she say things like that about you! You just leave her to me. I'll go and see her, first thing tomorrow morning. Forget about her for the moment. Go out and play with your friends and I'll call you when your tea's ready."

As soon as Mrs Robinson took the little monkey from his back, Frank immediately forgot about school and happily went out to play.

It was not long before Angela arrived home. She had been to a friend's birthday party but she certainly didn't look very happy about it. She also was carrying a small monkey on her back and her mother even suspected she may have been crying:

"What's the matter, love? Was the party not very nice?"

"It was awful, mum. Some of the girls called me names. They said I was a cissy and mummy's darling. I hate them!"

"Never mind, darling. You just tell me who those horrible girls were and I'll tell their parents exactly what's been going on. You just get changed now and go out to

play. I'll give you a shout as soon as your tea's ready. Here, let me take that monkey off your back."

This was typical of Mrs Robinson. She was a very kind lady, well liked by many friends who often called to see her during the day. She would always listen sympathetically to their problems and look concerned on seeing any monkeys on their backs. These friends would then go away, feeling a great sense of relief to have found such a sympathetic ear and a place where they could safely leave their monkeys.

As the days passed, however, Mrs Robinson began to feel tired herself. She was obviously not her usual self and seemed worried about something. She lost her zest for life and appeared unable to cope with her work as wife and mother. Often moaning and groaning now, in a most untypical manner, she began to worry both family and friends.

One day, a good friend took her on one side and spoke quite plainly to her:

"Listen, Sandra, I've been noticing lately how down you seem to be. Of course, you know what it is, don't you?"

"Well, I'm not really sure, Gladys. I've never really felt like this before. I suppose I'm just a bit run down. Been overdoing things lately, you know."

"You certainly have. The real trouble is all those monkeys you've got clinging to your back. And you're the only one who can do anything about it. The cure's in your hands. Send the monkeys away. They aren't yours, so why should you be carrying them? Get rid of them!"

"Do you think so?" mused Mrs Robinson. "Yes, I suppose I could just let them all go. After all, you're right. They don't really belong to me, so I think maybe I will just let them go away and see if they jump back on to the people they really belong to."

Within a matter of days, Mrs Robinson was her old self again. The monkeys had returned to wherever they belonged and she felt a new lease of energy. Now she was able and willing to help her family and friends again.

GENERAL SUGGESTIONS

Messages of the parable

- The most effective way of helping others.
- Difference between *genuine helping* and *rescuing operations.*
- Answers to the following queries:
  - In the way we go to others, are we "helpers" or 'rescuers"?
  - Why do we sometimes feel resentful towards those we try to help?
  - Why do we feel angry and irritated with those who love us?
  - Whom do we really try to help, others or ourselves? What is the motivation behind our helping relationships?
  - Are we manipulative in the way we try to "rescue" others?
  - Do we avoid "conflict" and "confrontation" to save others – or very likely ourselves – from those painful situations?
  - In our helping relationships, do we keep others dependent on us or give them absolute freedom?

Ideas and applications of the parable

- Mrs Robinson was not a "genuine helper" but a "rescuer". She took upon herself everybody's problem, without *helping them to help themselves.*
- She kept others dependent, without giving them a chance of growing and taking responsibility for their lives.
- In the end, she felt "crushed", "taken advantage of" and "resentful".
- Whom was she helping: others or herself (by boosting her self-image)?
- She should have confronted her husband and children, rather than rescuing them and taking their problems on her back.

- Mrs Robinson's friend, Gladys, was a genuine helper. She confronted her and helped her to face the real problem.

- Genuine helping is giving assistance to people
  - who are in real need,
  - who cannot help themselves,
  - who want to be helped.

- Rescuing means helping people who
  - either are not in real need
  - or who do not want to be helped
  - or who wish to avoid the pain of confrontation by not saying or doing things to someone who would otherwise be able to help.

- Any "rescuing operation"
  - prevents people from growing,
  - generates resentment, anger and negative feelings, both in the "rescued" and in the "rescuer",
  - curtails people's freedom,
  - encourages over-dependence and infantilism,
  - inflates the "self-image" of the rescuer who then feels superior to the rescued,
  - implies lack of trust in the ability of others to help themselves,
  - mars their self-image,
  - implies fear, diffidence and lack of assertiveness, either in the "rescued" or in the "rescuer" or in both.

- Reasons for being a "rescuer" are multiple: over-protectiveness, possessiveness, false pity for others, fear of losing those we love, distrust of others, superiority complex, perfectionistic tendencies, manipulation, paternalism, maternalism, protectionism, discounting of others, need to boost one's self-image, authoritarianism, inability to say no, fear of confrontation, inflated sense of responsibility, propensity to be regarded as a "nice person", compulsive fixation to help...

- Remedies to stop being a "rescuer" are:
loving people as they are, accepting them unconditionally, respecting people's freedom, accepting
conflict and confrontation as part of life, letting people
suffer (not making things too easy for them), allowing people to learn by making mistakes, expressing
one's feelings honestly, not forcing one's own expectations on others, not helping purely from a sense of
duty, not expecting returns from others, not blaming
others, not creating feelings of guilt, helping others
to help themselves, being available but unobtrusive,
not making people feel obligated, refusing to carry
the "monkeys" of others on our own backs.

New Testament texts in keeping with the ideas of the parable

New Testament texts in keeping with the ideas of the parable

In the Gospel we see that Jesus was a great "helper" but
never a "rescuer". He helped those in real need who
wanted to be helped. Examples:

Mt 8:1-4	Jesus makes a leper clean.
Mt 14:13-21	Jesus feeds the 5,000 in the desert.
Mt 15:21-28	The Canaanite woman.
Mk 3:1-6	The man with a crippled hand.
Mk 5:25-34	The woman with a flow of blood.
Mk 8:22-26	A blind man.
Mk 9:14-29	A boy with an evil spirit.
Mk 10:46-52	Bartimaeus.
Jn 5:1-18	Healing at the pool.
Jn 8:1-11	The woman taken in adultery.
Jn 11:1-44	Lazarus.

Jesus left people free. He never put anyone or told us to
put anyone under compulsion:

Mt 13:24-30	Allow the cockle to grow along with the wheat.
Mt 21:28-32	No one is forced to work in the field.
Lk 6:37-42	Do not judge.

Lk 15: 11-32	The father of the prodigal son leaves him free to go out.
Lk 19:1-10	Zacchaeus: Jesus invites him, does not force him.
Jn 4:1-42	Jesus invites the Samaritan woman, does not force her.
Mk 1:14-20	Jesus
Mk 2:13-14	invites
Mk 3:13-19	his disciples.

21

The Samaritan's predicament

A man was going down from Jerusalem to Jericho, when robbers attacked and stripped him, leaving him half-dead. A Samaritan witnessed the incident and was moved to compassion. He lifted up the victim and carried him to a nearby inn.

"Look after this man", he told the inn-keeper. "Spend whatever is necessary for his treatment and, on my return, I'll pay you everything."

Next day, the same Samaritan discovered another victim of robbers lying by the side of the road. He took him also to the inn and gave the same instructions to the inn-keeper.

The scene repeated itself regularly during the following days and, each time, the Samaritan performed the same good deed.

"Look!" cried the exasperated inn-keeper, "will you stop bringing in these people. It's an inn I'm supposed to be running, not a hospital! If things go on at this rate, I'll soon run out of business."

Now at a loss about what to do, the Samaritan discussed the problem with three friends. They each gave him good advice.

"Quite frankly," said the first friend, "there's nothing you can do. It isn't your problem, so just forget about it. It's the government's responsibility."

"I don't know about that", ventured the second friend. "I certainly feel sorry for the victims and we must do something to help. I have an idea..."

This friend bought the inn, which he then converted into a nursing-home. After searching the roads night and day for victims of attack, he soon filled it to capacity and began tenderly treating all the new patients.

The third friend was meanwhile adopting a totally different approach:

"We need to raise an armed task-force to root out these robbers and rid the country of their menace."

This is exactly what he did and many robbers were promptly shot on sight.

But things went from bad to worse and the original nursing-home was filled to overflowing. Some people suggested opening new nursing-homes and hospitals but there was an obvious limit as to what could be done.

The robbers were becoming more highly organised and could easily out-smart any task-force which opposed them. Violence simply bred violence and the troubles escalated. A group of good Samaritans met to discuss the implications.

"We need to make a rational assessment", insisted the first speaker. "We have been acting with our hearts and not with our heads. Instead of approaching all victims with love and confronting all robbers with hatred, let us appoint a commission of experts to study the problem in all its dimensions. We'll then learn the causes and discover what can be done to rectify the situation."

Such a commission did indeed deliberate and eventually tabulated the following conclusions:

1. The people between Jerusalem and Jericho are extremely poor.
2. They have no independent means of livelihood.
3. They are bonded labourers and daily wage-earners.
4. Whenever the crops fail, they are deprived of their only means of subsistence.
5. In the absence of remunerative work, they resort to robbery.
6. This present situation has not always existed.
7. It is clear that these people were economically self-sufficient and peace-loving in days gone by.
8. Since then, however, some outsiders came to the area.
9. These aliens dispossessed the original settlers and, through usury and other malpractices, reduced them to bonded-labourers and slaves.
10. The outsiders are now landlords and money-lenders, while the original settlers are no more than their slaves.

All the Samaritans were impressed with these findings. They realised that, instead of tending the victims of robbery and instead of attacking the robbers, they needed to solve the root causes of unrest.

The commission was therefore invited to deliberate again. Its chairman finally reported:

"Friends, we have found it difficult to agree on any single solution. In fact, we have arrived at as many conclusions as there are experts among us. I accordingly now invite each member to address you in turn."

"We must try to convert the exploiters, landlords and money-lenders", announced the first expert. "We need to meet them, change their hearts, tell them about the love of God. If we can convince them that the poor are their brothers, that we are all children of God, they will soon part with their ill-gotten wealth."

The second member suggested that all hopes lay in the

youth: "The children of these exploiters will be the society of tomorrow. My advice is to invest in better schools where they could be taught to share their goods and to realise the errors of their parents. Support needs to be encouraged for charitable and philanthropic organisations, through which children of the rich could learn to distribute food parcels, second-hand clothes and free medicines to the poor. They might also enjoy promoting dances and fetes in aid of those exploited by their parents."

"I too believe in education", voiced the third member, "but in education for all. This must include the children of the poor, who need equal opportunities to compete with the rich. The poor must learn to compete on the social ladder and to secure important and lucrative employment in tomorrow's world. My plea is for at least 20% or 30% of places in our schools to be open to the poor."

"All this talk of education!" countered the fourth speaker. "It's not heads but bellies that need filling. Concentrate on giving more food to the poor. If they weren't so hungry, they would soon stop attacking people. Satisfy their immediate needs by growing more food and, if necessary, by importing the right kinds of food from elsewhere."

"I totally agree", exclaimed the fifth member, "but I would go further. You see, I'm very concerned about human dignity and it worries me to think of the poor as mere recipients of charity. By all means, feed and clothe them but not to the point of personal embarrassment. They would feel much happier if they could earn their food and clothing, so let us establish work projects. If they built roads, canals, schools and other public buildings, the poor could be justly rewarded."

"Give a man a fish", began the sixth speaker, "and you feed him for a day. Teach him to fish and you feed him for life. I'm sure you've all heard that saying before. We must encourage these poor people to make better use of resources. There are many barren plots of land, which no one has ever bothered about. These could be irrigated, crops planted there and tended. The poor must be taught to do this and, I assure you, both they and ourselves would be surprised at how much good could be produced!"

"But why should the poor have to irrigate barren land?" demanded the seventh expert. "They were neither poor nor trouble-makers in days gone by. Only exploitation robbed their ancestors of prosperous living. My solution is therefore quite simple. Give them back their lands."

The chairman began to look very worried. Reluctantly he interrupted this last speaker:

"My dear colleague, we have been appointed to solve problems, not to create new ones..."

"Mr Chairman", continued the expert, "it is far from my intention to exacerbate present troubles. My contention is simply that we should help the poor not so much economically as politically. Instead of teaching them irrigation, we must politicise them, make them aware of their rights. They must realise their equality in the eyes of the law and that they are equal in freedom and dignity to any other citizens."

"Thank you", concluded the chairman. "Thank you for this very interesting suggestion but perhaps we ought to approach the matter with caution. After all, such poor people are not used to standing on their own feet. A taste for power might easily go to their heads and, once the flood-gates are opened... Well, you know, Christ and all great saints and thinkers have always preached charity to the rich and resignation to the poor..."

The Samaritans then began to debate the various solutions proposed. After often heated discussion, their love of charity and peace finally triumphed and they voted unanimously for solution X.

Messages of the parable

- Awareness of the social problem.
- Awareness of the real causes of poverty, hunger and want.
- Value of attempts to solve social problems and extent to which they have failed.
- Examination of solutions with regard to circumstances peculiar to our own part of the world.
- The need to arouse people from lethargy and to prod them into action.
- Solutions must not be limited to problems of injustice, oppression and exploitation at a sentimental level. Scientific, pragmatic and realistic approaches are all necessary.
- The self-satisfaction felt in contributing to charitable causes must give way to a realisation that this is often no more than elementary justice, let alone charity.
- We are all part of the problem, because we live inside it; without our active involvement, this problem will never disappear and the world cannot possibly improve.

Ideas and applications of the parable

- The events enacted between Jerusalem and Jericho are symbolic of today's events at a cosmic level.
- Today's wars, robberies, rapes, murders, drug trafficking, exploitation and terrorism are too awesome for easy solutions.
- Some good Samaritans try to solve those problems but without success, as the problems seem to multiply and diversify.
- The good Samaritans in this parable tackled the problem at an emotional level, either approaching victims with "pity" or robbers with "hatred".
- A better approach would have been to move from

emotion to fact, calling for a cool, scientific and realistic assessment of the situation.

- Many solutions have seemed good as far as they go but they do not go far enough; no simple solution will solve such multi-faceted problems.
- Any solution must be based on *justice* and *respect for human dignity*. The seventh member made a suggestion which may be the starting-point of any ministry in the pursuit of solving the social problem.
- Charity is not enough, if we only equate it with pity, commiseration, helping people in difficulties. Charity presupposes justice, which demands giving to others what is strictly owing to them: their rights, freedom and dignity.
- Class prejudices, vested interests, social snobbery – all blind us to injustices done to others.
- Afraid of radical change, we are content to settle for an unjust and oppressive *status quo* under the guise of "peace and order".
- Our thinking is clouded by such misleading assumptions as "development is directly proportional to economic growth", "improvement simply requires a change of heart", "democracy safeguards the rights of peoples", "consumerism is a universal panacea for all the ills of the body politic", "Marxism provides the only scientific interpretation of history".
- Any solution must involve an acceptance of basic human rights, human equality, freedom and dignity, a restoration of human values denied by injustice, oppression and exploitation.
- Any practical solution must recognise that the human heart is the source of what happens in the world and that no change can be effected without changing the hearts of individuals. But a change of heart is not enough. It is only the starting point towards abolishing unjust structures and building more equitable and humane ones.

New Testament texts in keeping with the ideas of the parable

Mt 5:1-11	The Beatitudes: change of heart.
Mt 6:1-4	Helping others.
Mt 6:24-34	God and possessions.
Mt 10:5-10	The mission of the Twelve: give freely...
Mt 23:13-28	Jesus condemns the hypocrisy and greed of the Pharisees.
Mt 25:31-46	The Last Judgement.
Mt 26:14-16	Money corrupts Judas.
Mk 10:17-27	Our hearts become attached to money.
Lk 1:46-55	Canticle of Our Lady.
Lk 3:3-20	Preaching of John the Baptist. Social content.
Lk 4:16-21	Jesus's mission. Synagogue of Nazareth.
Lk 10:25-37	The Good Samaritan.
Lk 12:13-21	The rich fool.
Lk 12:32-34	Riches in heaven.
Lk 16:14-15	The Pharisees' love of money.
Lk 16:19-31	The rich man and Lazarus.
Lk 19:1-10	The conversion of Zacchaeus, the exploiter.
Lk 20:45-47	The Pharisees exploiting widows.
Acts 2:43-47	All things
Acts 4:32-35	in common.
Acts 5:1-11	Ananias and Sapphira. Living for money's sake.
1 Tim 6:1-10	False teaching on riches. Greed for money is the root of all evil.
Jas 1 :9-11	Poverty and riches.
Jas 2:1-7	Warning against prejudice and the rich.
Jas 2:14-22	Faith in action.
Jas 5:1-6	Warning to the rich.
1 Jn 3:11-18	Love your brothers.

22

A spidery world

Spiders had been spinning their webs in exactly the same way for as long as any of them could remember. Some webs were thin, others thick, according to the individual strength and ability of the spider concerned.

One day, a particularly observant and deep-thinking spider began to muse upon the behaviour of human beings, a species of creature which spiders had long regarded as the most intelligent and progressive of creatures. "Why is it that human beings are constantly improving themselves?" thought this reflective spider. "They seem to grow richer and more powerful every day."

Noticing a television screen illuminated in a corner of the room, the spider was intrigued to witness a politician addressing the nation in the most optimistic terms:

"My dear people, we have embarked on the road to unlimited progress. Our party has given you a higher standard of living and a better life-style than you could ever have dreamed of. Such prosperity will continue. Poverty will finally be abolished and, with the accumulated wealth of our industrial and agricultural programmes, you shall all be able to purchase better homes and furnish them with everything you have ever desired."

Next day, the spider was equally intrigued to see, on the same television screen, an interview with a politician from another country. The message appeared very similar:

"In our country, we are pledged to support the glorious revolution of the proletariat. This will banish all poverty and suffering for ever and set us well on the road to unlimited progress. Our State-owned factories and farms will supply goods to be shared by all citizens."

Although full of admiration for both politicians, the Spider felt nevertheless depressed and rather ashamed:

"How clever and determined human beings are. But we spiders, what do we do to improve ourselves? For as long as anyone can remember, we have always spun our webs in exactly the same way. We are underdeveloped and must now try to reform such a dull and unimaginative attitude!"

The spider called a meeting of other spiders, exhorting them to greater efforts in the name of greater prosperity and unlimited progress:

"Brother and sister spiders, comrades! We are backward, lacking either imagination or ambition. This state of affairs can no longer be tolerated. Just look at human beings. They are creating for themselves unlimited progress in their affluent capitalist empires and in their prosperous proletarian societies. We spiders must not lag behind but must compete with human beings. More effort is called for!"

"Yes!" agreed another enthusiastic spider. "We must improve our image. We have nothing to lose but our dull, uninteresting and totally obsolete webs! Why not show more imagination and spin these in a more creative and more productive way?"

"You're right!" exclaimed another delighted member of the audience. "We should even go further. Let us diversify, produce even more goods and be bold enough to export some of our produce."

It was finally agreed that their spider economy must expand, with both a greater production and a greater willingness to consume more goods. As an initial step, everyone would spin bigger and better webs and spiders must help one another through newly-formed co-operatives.

With painful efforts of mind and body, their new webs were soon everywhere in evidence. From the tops of mountains, an observer looking down on forests could see vast stretches of web casting shadows as they hung between trees. Some webs needed to span surprisingly large distances between trees but the spiders' technology always seemed able to cope.

Yet the leaders of this new spidery revolution were still not content. Greater efforts continued, until not only trees were joined together but resources were pooled between certain co-operatives and soon webs could even be seen stretching from hill-top to hill-top and eventually from one mountain peak to another. The next aim, in this path to unlimited progress, was total co-operation, so that a web could be spun around the whole earth.

By straining themselves to the absolute limit, the spiders were soon producing the strongest and most silky web that could ever have been imagined. Within a very short time, all its gaps would indeed be filled. Exhausted but proud, the spiders confidently anticipated this final stage. Just one more effort and their gigantic web would encompass everything.

What a great triumph! How proud the spiders were of themselves but, next morning, they were all dead, exhausted and withered, caught in the biggest, most beautiful and most luxurious web any spider could possibly have imagined.

GENERAL SUGGESTIONS

Messages of the parable

- Myths prevalent in today's world: "consumerism", "omnipotence of science", "limitless progress", "classless society".
- The philosophy of "consumerism", of "produce more, consume more", is a suicidal course.
- The real danger is not from capitalism or communism but from consumerism. Both capitalist and communist states are "consumerist".
- Ideologies of both societies, although apparently contradictory, nevertheless share the same aims of world domination, economic exploitation and cultural colonialism.
- We are in danger of "cannibalising" our planet, by over-consuming and over-exploiting its natural resources.
- The only solution for world peace, justice and equity lies in thrift, moderation, equitable distribution of wealth, rationalisation of production and proper husbanding of natural resources.

Ideas and applications of the parable

- The spiders symbolise modern consumerist society, based on values concerned with material needs, such as cars, video-recorders, beauty aids, etc. Yet these "needs" are, in reality, only distractions, forms of escapism.
- By cannibalising on itself, sucking its own life-blood, our society's own superabundance contains within itself the seeds of decay and death.
- The spiders' webs symbolise status symbols: "the good life", "a lucrative job", "keeping up with the Joneses", "elitist institutions", "prefabricated pleasures", "escapist travel", "televised heroism".
- Just like the spiders, who wish to spin bigger and better webs, we seek to create the best of all possible

worlds but refuse to admit that there are limits to both our own resources and to those of the earth.

– When the webs become bigger and better, the spiders' physical resources inversely grow smaller. The closer they come to realising their dreams, the closer they come to self-destruction.

– Finally, in their all-consuming passion to achieve unlimited progress, the spiders exhaust themselves, just as they thought themselves on the point of success.

Bible texts in keeping with the ideas of the parable

Eccles 5: 10-20	Anyone who loves money never has enough.
Sir 10:9-11	What has a man to be so proud of?
Sir 14:3-6	Possessions do not bring enjoyment.
Sir 31:1-8	Gold is a pitfall. Every fool is caught in it.
Mt 5:1-10	The Beatitudes.
Mt 6:24-34	No man can serve two masters.
Mt 13:44-46	The parable of the hidden treasure.
Mk 10:17-31	The rich young man.
Lk 6:34-36	Lend without expecting returns.
Lk 12:13-22	The rich fool.
Lk 12:33-34	Riches in heaven.
Lk 16:19-31	The rich man and Lazarus.
1 Tim 6:1-10	Love for money is the root of all evil.
Jas 2:1-7	Warnings against prejudice.
Jas 2:14-17	Faith in action.
Jas 4:1-6	Friendship with the world.
Jas 5:1-6	Warnings against the rich.

23

The cows

The cows grazed happily in the meadows. There was always fresh grass there and lots of water in the nearby ponds. Occasionally a calf would be born, adding to the growing population and increasing the general prosperity.

One of the cows confided to her neighbour:

"Have you noticed how many new calves have been born recently? You know, if things go on at this rate, the meadow's likely to become overcrowded before too long."

"Yes", added another cow, who happened to overhear. "I was just saying the other day that we might do well to fence in the best parts of the meadow. In that way, we'll make sure there's still enough for us."

A few of the cows no sooner heard these arguments than they immediately set about enclosing some of the best pastures and ponds for themselves. Secure in their knowledge that they would always have plenty to eat and drink, they nevertheless had to deal with various approaches from cows now on the other side of the fence. Those were by far in the majority but could only look on enviously at their more intelligent neighbours who had taken possession of the best grazing land.

"Please can we have some of your grass and water", one of them pleaded. "We are starving and cannot feed our little ones."

The rich cows generously agreed to help their poor neighbours but only in exchange for milk: "After all, it'll be our grass and our water which will enable you to produce that milk."

The poor cows, of course, had no choice and freely agreed.

Soon the enterprising cows began to develop their estate and built large stables. Into these they invited the others, whom they would then be able to supervise more easily but, once again, in return for more comfortable living conditions:

"You may find conditions rather cramped but at least you'll be sheltered from bad weather and have an ample supply of food and water, as long as you continue to produce milk for us."

And produce milk they certainly did. It was stored in increasingly bigger tanks but still there seemed to be more than could possibly be handled. The business was therefore diversified, with huge quantities of cream, butter and cheese next being produced.

Skilled marketing techniques were used to trade these dairy products for other goods and even a profitable export trade was put into operation. Luxury items soon abounded and the capitalist cows began to engage the others not just in producing milk but also to work as domestics.

Yet, whenever these domestics were given free time to visit their families, they found still more striking contrasts between the two life-styles. The poor cows were cramped into even less space than before and they also seemed to have much less milk with which to feed their little ones.

Despite their appalling living conditions, however, the poor cows readily accepted that they must continue to work for their superiors. After all, they had freely entered into an agreement with them and so had really no cause for complaint.

It was only after many years that some of the younger poor cows began to question the system:

"Why should we just be 'milch' cows, working for others? Aren't we all from the same bovine race? We have the same rights to a high standard of living as any other cows! We need to claim our rights and stand united against oppression. Cows of the world unite! We have nothing to lose but our tethers!"

Forming themselves into a new revolutionary party, these young militant cows began organising a series of strikes. In the end, it proved quite easy to dethrone the original rulers and to assume control in their place.

A classless society of cows was proclaimed. Each member would give according to ability and be rewarded according to needs. Wealth would be shared equally, with all cows having equal rights, with no distinction of wealth or class.

Unfortunately, all those new hopes have still not been fulfilled. Many years have elapsed, during which most cows are still denied the freedom to roam wherever they will. Instead, the dominant bureaucracy of their reformed system has perpetuated the same practices, whereby the vast majority are still "milch" cows who continue to live in cramped conditions and must work hard for very small rewards of grass and water. Apparently they continue to do so freely but the promised bovine paradise on earth is far from a reality.

GENERAL SUGGESTIONS

Messages of the parable

- A study of the basic principles of both capitalism and communism.
- Questioning the legitimacy of the private ownership of the means of production.
- The theory of "surplus-value".
- Myths of capitalist ideology.
- Why the rich become richer while the poor become poorer.
- Workers' lack of freedom in a "free economy" market.
- Marxist ideology and its practice in communist countries are not the same things.
- Both capitalism and communism have forgotten God and our human spiritual nature, with the result that they *enslave*, rather than *free* human beings.
- Both systems have dehumanised and depersonalised human beings.

Ideas and applications of the parable

- Both systems treat a human being as *homo economicus*, for whom satisfaction of material needs constitutes the most important part of existence.
- While not denying our material needs, we contend that these are not our highest needs.
- As well as economic needs, we also have others which are intellectual, aesthetic, moral and spiritual. Unless all are satisfied, we shall never be fully human or fully alive.
- Capitalism is based on human greed, playing upon our competitive instincts to earn greater rewards than anyone else and upon our belief in the myth that happiness will automatically follow success.
- Communism is based on the myth in a Marxist paradise on earth ensuring that we must all give according to our capacity and receive according to our needs.

- Both systems fail to realise that the human heart ultimately makes the world what it is and that no system can change the world until human hearts change.
- Both capitalist and communist systems show no trace of humanity or reverence for the dignity of human persons.
- Both systems are "oppressive" because they have discarded the human soul.
- Both systems are "atheistic", "secularist" and "materialistic", catering only for material needs: communism in a totalitarian, depersonalised way, capitalism in a selfish, individualistic way.
- Both systems are caught in the "consumerism" trap, succumbing to the materialistic philosophy of "produce more, consume more".
- Both systems subscribe to the myth of indefinite economic perfectibility.
- In practice, both systems are "anti-God", "anti-Gospel" and "anti-human".
- Christianity cannot redeem capitalism, which is radically materialistic and anti-human, so that radical capitalism and Christianity are antithetic. Although it may also be totally opposed to communism, Christians would still do well to imbibe the many good features of Marxism: concern for the poor, equality, egalitarian ideals, equitable distribution of material goods, social justice.
- Whether they be Christians or Marxists, all people of goodwill should unite in the search for constructive and radical solutions to the world's problems.
- People of goodwill must show greater concern and commitment in helping to build a better tomorrow, where prosperity and opportunity may be available to all and not just to a privileged few.
- No effective and lasting solution can be imposed from above, whether by revolution or by peaceful change.
- Society can be changed through conscientisation, dialogue, persuasion and public education but change

has to be neither by force nor by repression. The process must not begin outside but only within the human heart, which is the source from which any real change can come.

– One of the greatest flaws in communism is that, while it works for the masses, it does not work with the masses.

Bible texts in keeping with the ideas of the parable

There are no Bible texts bearing directly on the topic of capitalism and communism but some texts do show us the true attitudes and values which we should adopt towards mankind, society, money and progress.

Ex 1 to 12	God frees his people from the slavery of Egypt.
	God does not satisfy only their material needs.
	The people's spiritual and moral needs are cared for.
Lev 6:1-5	God punishes the defrauders and exploiters.
Job 20:18-28	God's wrath
Job 24:1-4	and vengeance
Job 24:6-12	on the oppressors.
Amos 5:7-12	Woe
Amos 8:4-8	to the exploiters.
Prov 14:20-21	Blessings and curses.
Prov 15:5	Blessings and curses.
Prov 19:6-7	Blessings and curses.
Prov. 21:13	Blessings and curses.
Prov. 22:23-24	Blessings and curses.
Is 10:1-3	Do not oppress the helpless.
Sir 31:1-8	A rich man is subject to many worries.
Mt 4:1-4	Man does not live on bread alone.
Mt 5:1-11	The Beatitudes: change of heart.
Mt 6:19-21	Riches in heaven. "Where your riches are…"

Mt 6:24-34	You cannot serve two masters. Do not worry only about material needs.
Mt 9:35-38	Jesus's concern for people.
Mt 14:13-21	Feeding of the 5,000. Jesus cares for material needs.
Mt 16:5-12	The yeast of the Pharisees. It is not only bread that counts.
Mk 1:14-15	The first message of Jesus: Repent... turn your hearts...
Mk 10:17-31	The rich young man missed the best of life.
Mk 12:28-34	The great commandment. Without love for God and neighbour, no human society is possible.
Lk 3:1-14	The preaching of John the Baptist. Justice for all.
Lk 4: 16-22	Jesus's mission "socio-religious".
Lk 12:13-21	The rich fool. It is not only wealth that counts.
Lk 16:19-31	Social inequalities are condemned by Jesus.
Lk 19:1-10	Zacchaeus. It all begins with conversion of heart.
1 Cor 6:9-10	No exploiters will inherit the Kingdom of Heaven.
2 Cor 8:13-15	Share your abundance with others.
1 Tim 6:3-10	Enough is enough.
Jas 1:9-11	Poverty and riches.
Jas 2:1-9	Warning against prejudice.
Jas 5:1-6	Warning against the rich.

24

D—n it!

In a thick tropical jungle, there lived a large parrot population. Unfortunately, a group of settlers began reclaiming the land, cutting down many trees and building wooden houses.

It became fashionable for the settlers to catch the brightest and prettiest parrots, which they then put in cages to adorn their new homes and to entertain everyone with their amusing chatter. Soon there were thousands of captive parrots in cages, robbed of their natural freedom.

Some of the parrots still living in the jungle met to discuss the plight of their former friends:

"We must try to infiltrate into the houses where our poor brothers and sisters are now held captive", said Wilfrid, a less brightly-coloured parrot than most of the others but who was obviously dedicated to the new cause. "We must visit and comfort them in their hour of need."

At great risk to life and limb, the visiting began. Soon Anselm, one of the captive parrots, was being comforted by Terence, his generous visitor:

"Here, I've brought you some fresh fruits. The ones I know you like best of all. Think yourself lucky I was able to slip in unnoticed. Well, I'd better go now, before anyone catches me. Cheerio."

Patricia set about cheering up Miriam by singing her some of the songs she used to enjoy during her days of freedom:

"You know, my dear, I thought this would cheer you up and I'm also pleased to tell you that Wally and the children are coping very well. They've all asked me to send you their love. So, I may see you again soon. Bye."

Eddie felt very sorry for Jim and had come as soon as he possibly could, especially after hearing reports that the poor fellow might even be on the verge of suicide:

"I was so worried about your stomach trouble. I know it can't be easy for you but, here, I've brought you some of those bitter herbs that usually do the trick. Try not to worry too much and I'll call in again as soon as I can. That is, if I can avoid your owner's great big cat again. He nearly had me just then. I lost a couple of feathers in the process but, still, not to worry. I should be all right. Well, so long, then."

And so the visiting continued, despite the obvious risks to the kind visitors. They always did their best to brighten the lives of the unfortunate captives and, in the process, could go back to the jungle feeling rather pleased with themselves for having shown such kindness to others.

Obviously not appreciating this kind of service, Damian snapped back at Joe, one of his most persistent visitors:

"D—n it! Just push off, will you! Leave us all in peace. All you free parrots seem to do is bring food and medicine, cheerful good news about our families and advice on how best to settle down in captivity. I'm sick of all your charity and kind words. You can d—d well keep them! The only thing I long for is what you and your friends certainly don't seem to be capable of organising. So, just push off, you and all those other d—d cowards!"

Messages of the parable

- In today's world, the old law of the jungle that "might is right" still prevails.
- "Paternalism" in our approach to helping the poor and oppressed.
- Help for weaker members of society often consists only of palliatives, touching the periphery of a problem without going right to the core.
- We are frequently deluded into thinking we have done our duty when all we have done is to throw a sop to the poor.
- We must examine why resentment is sometimes felt by those we try to help.
- The poor and oppressed will never regain their freedom and rights without organising themselves and helping one another.

Ideas and applications of the parable

- The jungle symbolises our world, with the new settlers as powerful and influential people, while the parrots are ordinary people.
- Since, in the jungle, "might is right" and the law of tooth and claw reigns, the settlers took possession of the land and caged the parrots.
- The jungle, including its parrots, were their property.
- The free parrots felt pity for their captive companions and, wishing to help, believed that food, medicines, comfort and advice were all they could give.
- But they never thought of giving freedom by opening their friends' cages.
- The captives therefore felt resentment and anger.
- Yet the free parrots felt elated and proud at what they had done.
- They failed to understand why the captives were so resentful and ungrateful.

- Failure to open their companions' cages may have been an oversight or it may have been fear, self-interest or jealousy.
- In our world, everyone is born free but society robs many of their rights and freedoms.
- Socio-political structures have become "cages" for many citizens.
- Many are denied their socio-economic rights: the right to live a dignified life, the right to eat, to rest and to be clothed.
- In some countries, citizens are kept in iron cages; in others, the cages are silver and even golden but they are all still just cages.
- We must question the settlers' right to cage parrots, just as we must question the right of rich and powerful people to cage their disadvantaged neighbour by depriving them of their freedom and basic rights.
- Most social work is palliative, superficial and short-term. It does not go to the root of the problem, since we hardly ever ask why there should be any cases. Without daring to open their doors, we just throw sops to the caged.
- The poor, exploited and oppressed do not really want pity and sympathy, nor even food-parcels and second-hand clothes. They clamour for freedom, self-respect, justice, acceptance and equality.
- People of goodwill should not rest until every "parrot" in our world is free.
- "Free parrots" should stop playing into the hands of the masters of "caged parrots" by merely trying to make their friends' captivity bearable. They should do everything possible to give them the only thing they really need: their freedom.

Bible texts in keeping with the ideas of the parable

Old Testament:

Ex Ch. 1 to 12	The whole story of the liberation from Egypt. God frees his people from the oppression of Pharaoh.
Lev 6:1-5	Punishment to the defrauders and exploiters.
Job 20:18-28	God's wrath on the oppressors.
Job 24:1-4	Punishments
Job 24:6-12	to the oppressors.
Amos 5:7-12	Woe
Amos 8:4-8	to the exploiters.
Prov 14:20-21	Blessings and curses.
Prov 17:5	Blessings and curses.
Prov 19:6-7	Blessings and curses.
Prov 21: 13	Blessings and curses.
Prov 22:23-243	Blessings and curses.
Is 10:1-3	Do not oppress the helpless.
Is 58:6-11	True religion.
Jer 5:26-29	"Their houses are like a cage full of birds."
Sir 4:7-10	Help the down-trodden.

New Testament:

Mt 5:1-11	The Beatitudes. The mind of Christ.
Mt 6:19-21	Riches in heaven.
Mt 6:24-31	God and possessions.
Mt 6:24-34	You cannot serve two masters.
Mt 23:1-28	Jesus condemns the oppressive and exploitative behaviour of the Pharisees and the teachers of the Law.
Mk 12:28-34	The Great Commandment: Love your neighbour as yourself.
Lk 1:46-55	Canticle of Our Lady. God exalts the oppressed.
Lk 3:1-14	Preaching of John the Baptist.
Lk 4:16-21	The mission of Jesus: to free captives.

Lk 10:25-37	The Good Samaritan.
Lk 12:13-22	The rich fool.
Lk 16:19-31	The rich man and Lazarus.
Jn 13:1-17	Washing of the feet.
1 Cor 6:9-10	No exploiter shall possess the Kingdom of God.
2 Cor 8:13-15	Share your abundance with others.
1 Tim 6:3-10	Enough is enough.
Jas 1:9-11	Poverty and riches.
Jas 2:1-9	Warning against prejudices.
Jas 5:1-6	Warning to the rich.

25

What would you call it, Mum?

At exactly midnight, 1 January 1984, two babies were born just one hundred yards apart. One was born in a luxury flat, the other in an NHS hospital.

Baby Jason's parents were very rich. His father was a successful businessman and his mother owned large properties. Jason therefore felt happy, lying cosily in his clean new clothes. After his mother had given him a satisfying feed and put lots of talcum powder on his bottom, he slept contentedly in his comfortable new cot.

The other baby, Frank, had been born to poor parents. His father was a local council worker, who had just finished repairing the car-park of the hospital in which his son had been born. Frank was now trying to sleep in a council house but he was still hungry and felt uncomfortable in clothes handed down from his older brothers and sisters.

His mother, Betty, looked on helplessly, almost apologetically, as she whispered,

"Never mind, Frank, I'll make another bottle for you soon. We'll turn the heat up a little and see if that makes you settle down a bit better."

Jason's mother, Jayne, cooed affectionately to him, promising all sorts of new presents and a lovely summer holiday at their villa in Spain.

As the months rolled by, both babies continued to be loved by their parents, who fed and clothed them to the best of their ability. Jason's future, of course, was assured. He would soon be sent to a private preparatory school, then to a boarding school and eventually to Oxford or Cambridge. His father, Nigel, would be very happy to see him qualify as an engineer, a barrister or a doctor. He and Jayne agreed, however, that they would not force him into the kind of profession for which he was not suited but they preferred to leave the choice entirely to him.

"Why do I have to go to school, mummy?" asked Jason.

"Because you need to become clever like daddy and qualify for a good job, darling, where you'll be happy and rich, live in a comfortable house and have a beautiful wife and lovely children."

Betty and Tom knew that Frank would follow his brothers and sisters to the local school, which he would then leave at sixteen years of age. If he was lucky, he might be able to follow an apprenticeship and eventually qualify as a joiner, a plumber or an electrician. It was still much too early to know what kinds of work would then be available.

"Why won't you let me have a new bike like some of the other lads in the street?" asked Frank.

"Because we can't afford one", was Betty's curt reply.

"Why can't you have as much money as other people's mums and dads?"

"Because that's just the way things are", explained Tom.

"Some people just aren't cut out to be rich", sighed Betty despondently.

"How do you mean 'cut out', mum?" asked a bewildered Frank.

"Well, some people just call it 'bad luck', some 'fate', others 'your stars' or your horoscope'."

"But what would you call it, mum?"

GENERAL SUGGESTIONS

Messages of the parable

- Social and economic disparities exist because the fabric of our society is woven with justice and inequality.
- Social inequalities and discriminatory practices perpetuate themselves from one generation to the next by the very inner mechanisms of the status quo.
- Subterfuges are employed to disguise social inequalities and injustices, keeping people in ignorance by offering them such explanations as "luck", "fate", "fortune", "destiny" and "the stars".
- We "sacralise" inequalities and injustices by baptising them as "God's will", "providence", lulling victims into a false sense of resignation while, at the same time, securing for ourselves a certain "peace of mind".
- An emotional climate must be created, in which enthusiasm, generosity, kindness and love may help to alleviate the apparently hopeless situation of the exploited and the oppressed.

Ideas and applications of the parable

- The parable of Jason and Frank is too real to be classed as just a "story" but it forms part of everyday history.
- There is a danger that, in certain schools, children of the prosperous are programmed to be prosperous, while children of the poor are programmed to remain poor.

151

- The structuring of our society tends to perpetuate existing disparities between rich and poor.
- Moneyed people have at their disposal the resources needed to secure what they want and they can "pull strings" by using such means as the press and even government agencies and various legal means of increasing their wealth.
- Consciously or unconsciously, they will use these powers to protect their interests and those of their children.
- Having no education, no expertise and no influence, the poor and illiterate cannot compete with the rich and educated.
- In our highly competitive society, the poor will always lose in the rat-race, where the socially, financially and educationally handicapped cannot compete with the rich, highly literate and influential.
- The vaunted equality of rights and opportunities in modern society is often a smokescreen to hide the sordid reality.
- Tragically we sanitise and sacralise social injustices and discrimination by investing them with a "religious" aura, referring to them variously as "Divine Providence", "God's will".
- God cannot countenance evil, so no form of social injustice, economic exploitation, oppression or class distinction can ever be willed by God.
- Injustices, far from being the results of God's loving providence, are directly attributable to human malice, cruelty, greed, selfishness and man's inhumanity to man.
- Any religion conniving at injustice or blessing exploitation and discrimination only dishonours God and is not true religion but a terrible manifestation of the evil side of human nature only masquerading as religion.
- True religion means love of God and love of all human beings, including and especially the poor, the weak and the downtrodden.

- True religion means accepting the equality of all human beings as brothers and sisters.
- True religion is giving oneself to others "even unto death", as Christ did.

Bible texts in keeping with the ideas of the parable

Old Testament:

Deut 15:7-10	Be generous and open-handed.
Job 31:15-22	I have been generous.
Job 20:18-28	Punishments to those who exploit others.
Job 24:1-4	Reckoning to those
Job 24:6-12	who were unjust.
Amos 5:7-12	Punishments to the exploiters.
Amos 6:1-7	Evils that befall the super-rich.
Prov 14:20-21	Blessings and curses.
Prov 17:5	Blessings and curses.
Prov 19:6-7	Blessings and curses.
Prov 21:13	Blessings and curses.
Prov 22:23-24	Blessings and curses.
Jer 5:28-29	Blessings on the just and curses on the unjust.
Is 58:6-11	The kinds of fast and worship which God approves.
Sir 4:7-10	Help the downtrodden.
Sir 10:26-31	Be moderate in your life.
Sir 31:1-8	A rich man is subject to many worries; a poor man is not.

New Testament:

Mt 6:24-34	No man can serve two masters.
Mt 25:31-46	Parable of the Last Judgement.
Mk 10:17-31	The rich young man.
Lk 6:34-36	Lend without expecting return.
Lk 12:13-22	The rich fool.
Lk 12:33-34	Riches in heaven.
Lk 16:19-31	The rich man and Lazarus.

Jas 2:1-9	Warning against prejudices.
Jas 5:1-6	Warning the rich.
Jas 2:14-20	Faith in action.
1 Jn 3:11-18	Love one another.
2 Cor 8:13-15	Share your abundance.
1 Tim 6:7-10	Enough is enough.

26

God's judgement

On the day of retribution, God will divide all people into two groups, just as the shepherd separates the sheep from the goats. He will put the sheep at his right hand and the goats at his left. Then God will say to the people at his right:

"Receive the Kingdom prepared for you, ever since the beginning of the world. I was hungry and you fed me. I was thirsty and you gave me to drink. I was naked and you clothed me. I was sick and you cared for me. I was in prison and you visited me. Indeed, whenever you did any of these things to any of the less important among your brothers and sisters, you did it to me. Come now, my friends, be blessed with the joy of my presence and with my love."

Then God will turn to the others and say:

"I was hungry and you built five-star hotels and luxurious restaurants. I was naked and you founded a huge garment industry of superfine fabrics. I was sick and you opened expensive health centres. I was homeless and you built skyscrapers and luxury flats. I was lonely and you established golf clubs and elite cultural centres... I was illiterate and you built institutes of higher management. I begged for social justice and you used charity centres to give me second-hand clothes. I pleaded for my rights and you constructed bigger prisons. I was in need of protection from unjust exploitation and you invented tanks, submarines, missiles and nuclear warheads... I was in need of nothing more than a small country park, in which to meet my friends, and you provided bigger motorways. I longed to pray in privacy and you designed large cathedrals, mosques and temples. I wanted to communicate with my creator and you devised pompous, complicated and expensive rituals."

God will then say to all those on his left: "Get away from me, you accursed evil-doers! I do not know you."

GENERAL SUGGESTIONS

Messages of the parable

- Deep-rooted greed and selfishness rampant in our society.
- Functioning of socio-political structures in modern society.
- The sole aim of production is not service but profit.
- Intentionally or unintentionally, the prevailing politico-cultural apparatus tends to serve the interests of intellectual and powerful elites.

- In many countries, a tiny percentage of the population consists of rich and powerful people living at the expense of a huge percentage of poor people.
- Our social system is based on many premises, values and ideals diametrically opposed to those of the Gospel.

Ideas and applications of the parable

- If there is progress, we must ask for whose benefit it is: rich or poor?
- Industry, education, socio-political institutions, cultural and medical centres are often designed to serve elitist interests; and not always excluded are the interests of some religious establishments.
- Is our economy planned to satisfy the needs of the masses or the greed of rich industrialists and big businessmen?
- "Capital" is interested in "profit-making" and "capital producing", not in "people-orientated" ventures.
- Industry continues to produce more and more sophisticated goods for a smaller and smaller number of people, the privileged few.
- Sacrificed to the "moloch of industry", the masses are mere cogs in a big soul-less machine set in motion by the rich and for the rich.
- Could the small percentage of the affluent attain their high standards without the often painful efforts of the huge percentage of their brothers and sisters?
- Perhaps the following questions need to be asked:
  • Whose interests are served by centres of higher education and research?
  • Through law-enforcement, do the poor and weak always have their rights safeguarded and defended?
  • Are the interests of poor people served by the high technology of satellites, atomic power stations and research centres?
  • Do well-trained military forces and sophisticated weapons defend the interests of the rich or those of the poor who have nothing to defend?

- Who enjoys the benefits of promoting hotel and tourist industries?

– Despite the erection of excellent hospitals and prestigious medical research centres, many people still die for lack of the most elementary health services.
– We have built great motorways to link cities but many people still live in deplorable conditions.
– We have built "charitable" and "humanitarian" homes for the poor, elderly and handicapped, in order to soothe our consciences by doling out alms, second-hand clothes and sub-standard food to these less fortunate member of society.
– God cannot but condemn a society rooted in greed, inequality, discrimination and injustice.

New Testament texts in keeping with the ideas of the parable

Mt 5:1-11	The Beatitudes: basic attitudes to build a just society.
Mt 6:19-21	Riches in heaven.
Mt 6:24-31	God and possessions.
Mt 20:20-28	Mother's request. Greed for power and influence.
Mt 23:1-28	Jesus condemns the hypocrisy and greed of the Pharisees. Our world is built on hypocrisy and greed.
Mt 25:32-46	The Last Judgement. Jesus condemns our selfishness.
Mk 9:33-37	Who is the greatest?
Mk 10:11-31	The rich young man.
Mk 12:28-34	The Great Commandment.
Lk 3:1-4	The preaching of John the Baptist.
Lk 4:1-13	Jesus was tempted to take advantage of his position to obtain riches, popularity and power.

Lk 10:25-37	The Good Samaritan.
Lk 14:7-11	The best places at the banquet. (Looking for the best place in the banquet of life.)
Lk 17:19-31	The rich man and Lazarus.
Lk 22:24-27	An argument of greatness.
Jn 13:1-17	The washing of the feet. Service should be our goal in life.
1 Tim 6:3-10	Love of money is the root of all evil.
Jas 1:9-11	Poverty and riches.
Jas 2:1-13	Against prejudice.
Jas 2:14-22	Faith in action.
Jas 5:1-6	Warning against the rich.

27

Eureka!

David and Stephen had graduated together from the same university and had then gained scholarships as research students. They were now working for the same internationally famous perfume company.

It had long been their ambition to discover a new formula and invent a perfume so rare and exquisite that it would enchant the world. Finally, after many years, they were able to exclaim, "Eureka! At last! We've found it!"

"What shall we do now?" wondered David. "I suppose we'd better take a sample along to the boss, straight away."

"No!" said Stephen, "not yet. We'll just keep it to ourselves for a little while longer. I'm sure we could find a very profitable market for it in the not-too-distant future."

They both agreed, for the moment, to sit tight. Their secret would go no further and only their wives would be allowed to wear the marvellous new invention.

David hurried home but, while still in his car, looking anxiously at the small sample of new perfume, he muttered to himself:

"I can't risk leaving it in a bottle like that. It'll start to evaporate. I'll have to find something better."

He stopped the car, went into a chemist's shop and bought a much more secure container. He then drove home to give such a wonderful present to his wife, Rachel.

"Look what I've brought for you, darling", he gasped. "We finally cracked it! We've invented the most wonderful perfume that's ever existed. And my sample's all for you. Here! Put some on. You'll be the envy of everybody. But we'll just keep quiet for a while about where it came from. We think we'll be able to make a huge profit if we play things carefully."

Rachel was overjoyed and, on every possible occasion, she wore the wonderful new perfume, delighting relatives and friends who could not help feeling jealous and very curious about the name of the shop where they could buy some for themselves. Eventually, when the last of the perfume had been used, Rachel unceremoniously threw away the bottle, knowing that David would soon bring her another sample.

Meanwhile, what had Stephen been doing? He also had hurried home with his sample but, instead of giving any to his wife, he was determined that not a drop of this fantastic new invention must be wasted. He called at an antique shop and bought a rare Ming jar. It was, of course, extremely expensive but he thought his money well spent and, with utmost care, he poured in the precious perfume.

Next day, still without letting anyone smell or even see the contents of his now priceless jar, he ordered a showcase in which it would be put on display. His wife and friends were spell-bound to see the beautiful exhibit but Stephen refused to let anyone even touch it. He put up a notice saying, "DO NOT TOUCH". When one of his children stretched out her hand towards it, he yelled: "Don't touch it! Can't you read? Don't ever touch it!"

Soon Stephen's life became entirely ruled by this jar. He was the only one who knew what it contained and he would constantly gaze at it in private. From morning till night, he would sit transfixed. Everything began to revolve round this jar. He even gave up working at the perfume laboratory, in order to spend more time looking at his pride and joy.

The months and years rolled by, with Stephen becoming increasingly transfixed in front of his showcase. When, at last, he died, his wife opened it and took out the Ming jar. She opened the lid to see if anything was inside but found nothing. The priceless jar was empty.

GENERAL SUGGESTIONS

Messages of the parable

- The "spirit" and "ideals" of any new movement need to be constantly preserved and cherished, lest they vanish.
- Any human society needs "laws", "structures" and "systems" as a framework within which to establish its self-identity, to express its purpose and to hold itself together.
- Once this framework loses its inner spirit, it becomes immobile, rigid, obsolescent and an empty shell.
- There is danger in turning means into ends when we lose sight of the "essence" of dogmas, rituals and organisations which are then merely pursued for their own sakes.
- There must be a continual dialectical tension between "spirit and law", "ideal and institution", "prophetism and organisation", "renewal and tradition", if any social or religious organism is to remain healthy and grow.

Ideas and applications of the parable

- David and Stephen discovered a new "essence", a precious perfume, which they both had to preserve from evaporation and waste.
- Both looked for some container, some "structure", to safeguard their treasure.
- David chose a functional container, a bottle that would fulfil his purpose but which, in quality, size and appearance, meant nothing. It was only a means to hold the perfume, which was the really precious thing and, when it was empty, Rachel simply discarded the bottle.
- Stephen looked for a precious and beautiful container and eventually fell in love with it. For him, it became more essential than the perfume.
- David's bottle was discarded when all the perfume had been used but Stephen clung to his vase long after his perfume had evaporated. Although only a container, a means to hold the perfume, it became for Stephen an end in itself.
- The moral of the parable may be applied to all human institutions.
- In order to preserve law and order and to progress, we need socio-political, economic and religious structures, through which we attain to culture, art, science and everything which enriches our lives.
- But there are dangers in "institutionalism", since laws, structures, codes of conduct and systems of belief have a relative, temporal and instrumental value. They are means, not ends.
- Unfortunately, they are regarded by many as "Ming jars" which cannot be touched and which must be preserved, at all costs, as ends in themselves.
- If they are to serve as means, for which they are really intended, they must be continually renewed, so as to respond to changing needs. Such renewal implies even the total discarding of whatever is redundant or obsolete.

- By absolutising the outward forms of legalism, literalism, ritualism, fundamentalism and structuralism, some people unconsciously become idol-worshippers, sacrificing the whole meaning and purpose of their lives on the altars of human structures and systems.
- Many of these worshippers are found in the areas of dogma and ideology, worshipping at their own exclusive shrines and uttering profanities just like anyone else. Witness politicians rigidly, artificially and statically divided into various political parties, or divided between capitalists and communists. Witness Christians similarly divided into Catholics, Protestants and Orthodox.
- Canon Law is only a "container" to store the quintessence of the Good News of Jesus, to preserve from the Gospel the true spirit, which is much more important than the law.
- Rules, vows and constitutions of religious congregations are "containers" of the charisms of their founders. While observing their rubrics, the religious must go beyond these to grasp the evangelical spirit which animated those founders.
- The impression is sometimes given that many Church laws and religious constitutions are empty "Ming jars".
- Many letters and instructions coming from higher authorities sound like Stephen's warnings: "Don't touch it! Can't you read? Don't ever touch it!"
- Has our socio-economic, political, cultural, artistic and religious world become a museum of "Ming jars"?

New Testament texts in keeping with the ideas of the parable

Mt 5:17-10   Teaching about Law. The all-important thing is to do what God requires.

164

Mt 5:21-22	"You
Mt 5:27-28	have heard
Mt 5:31-32	that it was said...
Mt 5:33-3	But now
Mt 5:38-39	I tell you..."
Mt 5:43-44	Jesus updates the Law.
Mt 7:28-29	Not everyone who calls me, "Lord, Lord..."
Mt 7:28-29	Jesus taught with authority – not the authority given to him by law.
Mt 9:14-17	Questions about fasting. New skins for new wine. New laws, new structures for new advances, new findings.
Mt 12:1-8	Questions about the Sabbath. The Sabbath
Mk 2:23-28	was made for man, not man for the Sabbath.
Mt 12:9-14	Healing on the Sabbath: keeping the Law
Lk 13:10-17	or the spirit of the Law?
Mt 15:1-20	What makes a person unclean? To break the law or the evil that is in that person's heart?
Mt 23:1-28	Jesus speaks against hypocrisy, Pharisaism, legalism.
Mk 11:27-33	On whose authority? The Pharisees wanted legal warrants.
Acts 15:1-35	The Jewish Law is discarded. No circumcision any more.
Acts 10:1-48	Customs are abrogated. There are no impure
Acts 11: 1-8	foods any longer.
Rom 3:9-31	We are saved
Rom 5:1-11	not by the Law
Rom 6:1-23	but because
Rom 10:1-21	of God's
Rom 11:25-37	accepting love.

28

The floating country

Skipland was a country composed of many islands. Prosperous and scientifically more advanced than their neighbours, its inhabitants were very happy. The only problem seemed to be one of over-crowding, since the population had been rapidly expanding but the sea set limits to further territorial expansion.

The scientists and planners worked hard and eventually reached a solution: huge pillars would be erected on the bed of the sea, strong enough to support gigantic platforms on which new cities could be built. Within only a few months, the country's great technological resources had created a new skyline, studded with high buildings, comprising schools, colleges, supermarkets, factories, theatres and churches.

"How lucky our children are", claimed one of the teachers. "We now have the finest schools in the world. Our pupils will develop into scientists more advanced than anywhere else."

"We already have the best hospitals anywhere", pronounced one of the doctors. "Soon every known disease will be conquered and our people will continue to be the healthiest ever."

"We are the happiest people in the universe", Ted, one of the workers, assured his employer. "Our future is secure and now we can just concentrate on enjoying life to the full."

A few weeks after official openings of various new buildings, Ted was relaxing on the beach when he noticed something strange. The sea seemed higher than usual and the platforms, on which the new cities were built, appeared closer to the surface of the water.

Fearing that the sea-bed might be collapsing, Ted hurried to inform the authorities. One of the borough engineers, however, was most dismissive of such a suggestion:

"Nonsense! We have absolutely no scientific data about such a preposterous eventuality. Our cities were designed by the world's best architects and constructed by the finest builders- Please don't waste our time by silly talk about the sea-bed collapsing!"

"But I've seen the evidence with my own eyes", insisted Ted.

"You must have been dreaming. Now, kindly leave us alone", was the borough engineer's final contribution to the discussion.

After leaving the Town Hall, Ted decided to attempt another approach. He called at one of the hospitals, where he begged the receptionist to set in motion some kind of evacuation for the patients. A doctor was immediately summoned. He pronounced Ted mad:

"What absolute rubbish! What's the matter with you? How do you think we could possibly move handicapped patients like ours without much better reasons than that?"

Ted next tried to save children in the schools. He was told that the schools were the best in the world. The tremendous amount of time and money invested in them made it unthinkable that they could ever sink.

"At least", thought Ted, "people will surely want to save their money." He therefore tried to warn staff in the local bank but they suspected him of trying to cause confusion and panic, so that he might be able to stage a robbery. The police were called and Ted was arrested.

Next morning, throughout the world, millions of people read newspaper headlines:

THOUSAND DROWN!
FLOATING COUNTRY SINKS!

GENERAL SUGGESTIONS

Messages of the parable

- Many maladies affecting the modern world are symptoms of a collapse in the very basis of our society.
- Finding remedies for such ills would only be a patchwork solution and, instead, we need to restructure our society from its very foundations.
- We need critically to evaluate the relevance of our "traditional" ministries to the conditions and demands of modern living.
- We must investigate these ministries with a new urgency, in order to meet the challenge posed by a technological society which, borne on a tidal wave of "unlimited progress" and "omnipotence" is rushing away from God towards its own destruction.
- We need to consider preparing, on an emergency footing, the ground for a new, just, equitable and stable social order.

Ideas and applications of the parable

- Skipland was prosperous, technologically advanced and proud of its accomplishments, being able to boast many fine institutions and buildings.
- Its people were secure and self-complacent, unaware of how their country's entire substructure was gradually sinking into the sea-bed.
- Had they realised what was happening, the Skiplanders would have done well to question the relevance of those great achievements to their individual lives.
- Skipland symbolises our world, whose scientific and technological advances have brought us so much material progress.
- Should we not ask ourselves the questions which the Skiplanders did not ask?
- Is not the very basis of our society falling apart?
- If so, should we continue erecting bigger and better buildings or should we not mobilise resources to salvage the tottering structure of our society?
- Without neglecting our traditional ministries of teaching, nursing, evangelising, etc., should we Christians not rush to save the world by building a better social order?
- We face an awesome scenario: ecological pollution, plunder of natural resources, threats of an atomic holocaust, disruption of international relations, a population explosion, human exploitation on an international scale, millions dying from poverty and hunger, obsolescence of traditional socio-political structures, a loss of the meaning of life. It is time we wakened up to our fundamental barbarism and did something about it.
- It is time we asked ourselves how relevant are our traditional ministries with their domestic concerns and parochial interests, compared with the gigantic problems facing us and the collective evil in our midst.
- When a ship is sinking, what is the use of serving

meals to a few passengers who are hungry or sticking band-aids on members of the crew injured in trying to save lives?

- We need to free many people from traditional ministries and allow them to become actively involved in establishing a new social order and building the Kingdom of God in the "here and now".
- Each ministry should be given a new orientation and we should muster all people of goodwill to save our "Skipland" from submerging.
- Some modern thinkers have tried to build the foundations of our society on the soil of bourgeois materialism, trusting not in God but in their own skill and power. Now that society is crumbling, they are not willing either to own up to their errors or to let other people speak the truth.
- Ted, the prophet of Skipland, tried to open the eyes of his fellow-citizens but he was finally arrested by the police. Christ was crucified for rebelling against the standards of the materialist society of his day. All honest social reformers continue paying a price for their attempts to remove the evils staring us in the face.
- We have to change people's hearts if we want to build a new world. It is not possible to build "new and better" structures if the hearts of the builders do not become "new and better".

New Testament texts in keeping with the ideas of the parable

There are no texts bearing directly on the theme of the parable. We can only comment on some of them to strengthen the points made in the parable.

1. Jesus begins his ministry:

Mt 4:17	The Kingdom of Heaven is near.
Lk 4:16-30	The commission given to Jesus: preach the Good News to the poor; proclaim

	liberty to captives; set free the oppressed; announce the salvation of God.
Mt 5:1-11	The Beatitudes: the need for a change of heart, of values.
Mt 5, 6, 7	The Sermon on the Mount: Jesus proposes a new way of looking at life, at people and things. A radical change.

2. John the Baptist's preaching:

| Mt 3:1-12 | The kingdom of Heaven is near. |
| Lk 3:1-18 | Urgency of the task. Change your hearts. Radical change. |

3. The parables of the Kingdom:

Mt 13:24-30	The weeds.
Mt 13:31-32	The mustard seed.
Mt 13:33	The yeast.
Mt 13:44	The hidden treasure.
Mt 13:45-46	The pearl of great price.
Mk 13:47-50	The net.
Mk 2:21-22	New patch and new wine skins.
Mk 4:26-29	The growing seed.
Lk 14:15-24	A great feast.

4. Other texts:

| Lk 1:46-56 | Canticle of Our Lady: "He scattered the proud... brought down mighty kings... lifted the lowly..." |
| Lk 10:1-12 | The sending of the seventy-two disciples. "The Kingdom of God has come near you." |

29

Uncivilised!

A group of tourists chanced to land on a remote island lost in the South Pacific. They were amazed to discover there a part of the world not yet "graced" by civilisation but inhabited by "savages".

When such startling news reached the civilised world, reporters from the press, radio and television immediately began investigations. One of the newspaper accounts will suffice to speak for them all. First the headline:

UNCIVILISED SAVAGES FOUND
EVEN AS LATE AS
THE END OF THE 20th CENTURY

A group of tourists has discovered a new island in the South Pacific. Its inhabitants seem completely uncivilised.

They drink pure crystal water from springs and rivers. They still refuse to drink various beers, liqueurs, carbonated drinks and other beverages offered to them by one of our special correspondents.

FRUIT
Neither do they eat sterilised pre-cooked food but seem to prefer only fresh fruits from their own island.

They live entirely in small villages and have never experienced big-city life.

ON FOOT
They walk on foot, since none of them own cars, motor bikes, helicopters or aeroplanes. They had never even heard of bicycles!

They do not use telephones but, instead, talk with one another, face-to-face, for hour after hour, apparently in the most friendly way. Telex and Fax machines, video recorders, televisions and even transistor radios are totally absent from their lives.

LIVING

None of the children go to school but spend all their time playing. Apparently, it is claimed, they "learn from living".

All the inhabitants are staunch believers in God, to whom they pray for whatever they might need. They believe in life after death, when they hope to share happiness with God.

RELAXED

They are relaxed and calm, sleeping soundly without barbiturates, sedatives or sleeping pills of any kind. No one had ever heard of an ECG and psychiatrists are totally unknown on this amazing island.

These inhabitants are surprisingly sturdy and, some would say, even witty. Not a single death has been recorded from heart attacks and no incidence of either high blood pressure or thrombosis has yet been found.

EMPLOYMENT

One of our most extraordinary findings is that there are no very rich or very poor! There are no employers or employees but only self-employed.

SEX

Observers declare that couples enjoy their love life without any sign of embarrassment, complexes or "fears of inadequacy".

UNBELIEVABLE

It is truly incredible that such underdeveloped, uncivilised and backward people can still be found today, near the end of the twentieth century.

GENERAL SUGGESTIONS

Messages of the parable

- The meaning of "civilisation".
- Supposed superiority of "Western culture".
- Criteria for defining civilisation.
- Relative and subjective connotations of the words "culture" and "civilisation".
- Cultures are many, different and unique, just like individuals.
- Arrogance in thinking that "our culture" is better than other cultures.
- The need to approach with humility people of other cultures, with different views and values. A desire to learn from them.

Ideas and applications of the parable

- Discovering people different from themselves, the tourists immediately branded them as "savages", "uncivilised" and "under-developed".
- What criteria were the tourists using to pass such judgements?

174

- Are we like those tourists, with regard to people of different cultures, tastes, beliefs and customs?
- Cultures and civilisations are "different" but no one is "superior" or "inferior" to any other.
- Culture has a "functional" role within a particular environment and group of people. This function of "culture" is to enable the people of a particular group and environment to live satisfying lives.
- Inasmuch as a culture fulfils this role for a particular group of people, it is the "best" culture for that group.
- Obviously "Western culture" would be functionally unsuitable to tribal and so-called backward peoples, to desert-dwellers, to the millions of inhabitants in the Indian sub-continent or to those of the Polar regions.
- Rich and technologically powerful, the West exports its culture to many parts of the world, while some Western countries have tried to impose their civilisation on some other areas of the globe.
- Some peoples, by accepting Western culture, may have unwittingly supported what could be a form of exploitative cultural colonialism.
- Each country, each group of people has to find out what is the best for itself. Poor countries – although not necessarily uncivilised – eagerly ape the customs and life-styles of affluent countries, thereby repudiating their own rich cultural heritage.
- The so-called "affluent society" is ruled by money. Poorer nations have bartered away both their natural and their artistic heritage to rich (both capitalist and communist) nations for a mess of pottage! It is only money which seems to count, not religion, poetry, language or art.
- A country's civilisation is now judged by its financial wealth. Even if its moral and spiritual values and its artistic sensibilities are thoroughly debased, it is still considered the most civilised if it has the largest pile of paper money and coins to shuffle in the stock market.

- So-called "modern civilisation" has robbed many peoples of their self-identity, their wholesome joys, justifiable pride in an historic past, their national genius, the priceless treasures of their language and culture, almost of their very souls.
- Culture should bring true joy but where does this now seem to lie? In wealth and material progress? No! True joy lies in being human, finding meaning in life, enjoying social intercourse, in friendliness, in self-acceptance and in trusting and loving God.
- What joy does "modern civilisation" offer to people whom it brands as "savages"? Cosmetics, transistors, videos, pre-cooked meals, alcoholic and non-alcoholic drinks, tabloid fiction, sports cars, speed-boats, tranquillisers.
- Modern "civilisation" is a Procrustean bed, into which every member of every group in every nation is forced to fit.
- In place of a heart, modern civilisation has machines, symbolising money, greed, status and power. There is nothing intrinsically wrong with machines but these should not rule human life; and human beings should use them in a manner which will bring real meaning, joy and satisfaction.
- Instead of being the basically good, dynamic and progressive force it had set out to be, modern civilisation has turned into a Frankenstein monster devouring all the cultures and civilisations that cross its path.

New Testament texts in keeping with the ideas of the parable

It is not possible to find texts directly bearing on the topic of this parable but we do find many texts in keeping with its key ideas:

Mt 5:1-11	The Beatitudes: true happiness.
Mt 6:24-37	God and possessions. Do not worry. Be contented.

Mt 7:1-6	Judging others. No group of people can judge any other group.
Mt 13:53-58	Jesus is rejected at Nazareth. He was judged inferior. He was not educated.
Mt 23:1-28	Jesus condemns the Pharisees. They thought themselves better, because of money and learning.
Mk 10:17-27	Money made the rich young man lose his happiness.
Lk 4:1-13	Jesus is tempted to be rich, popular and powerful.
Lk 12:13-21	The rich fool. "The worth of man (this could be said also of a country or civilisation) is not in what he owns but in what he is."
Lk 12:32-34	Riches in heaven.
Jas 1:9-11	Poverty and riches.
Jas 2:1-7	Prejudice.
Jas 4:1-6	Friendship with the world.

30

Glasses and lenses

A quaint custom arose, in bygone days, of putting special kinds of spectacles on new-born children. No one knows why or when this practice began but one of the effects was to distort the colours. Red appeared green, black looked like white and yellow like blue.

Another strange effect was to distort shapes. High appeared low, thin looked like fat and far like near. Most alarmingly of all was the way in which beauty and ugliness were interchanged and how kind people looked cruel and good people bad.

According to a person's racial origin, social class or religious persuasion, slight variations were introduced into the design of lenses. It therefore became commonplace for white children to see black children as horrible, and for members of different religious sects to despise one another.

In countries where these strange spectacles were used, it then became forbidden to remove them. At first, some people objected but, eventually, the law was accepted and nobody ever thought of challenging the wearing of those spectacles from birth to death. Most people would have been ashamed to question a practice which had become deep rooted into their particular culture. It has even been suggested that, with the passing of the years, few people realised that they were actually wearing spectacles!

Unfortunately, no controls were ever established about the number of variations introduced to the design of lenses for the many different groups within a community. Friction consequently increased at an alarming rate. Not only did blacks and whites hate one another and believers constantly argue with believers, but also men grew to despise women and women to ridicule men.

Quarrelling could be heard constantly, whether at home or in public places:

"All blacks are dirty and lazy!"

"All whites are exploiters and murderers!"

"All working-class people are inferior and worthless!"

"All professional people are thieves and proud!"

"There is no God! Anyone who believes in God is a fool. It's stupid to talk about a heaven being in the sky."

"Atheists like you are too dull and stupid to appreciate the wonders of God's creation. You're no better than animals! "

Before very long, quarrels degenerated into brawls and then brawls into armed warfare. Deaths inevitably followed in many instances.

In a world filled with hatred, private assassinations multiplied. Wars – both tribal and national – increased alarmingly. At last, a baby boy was born who one day had the courage to remove his spectacles.

Amazingly, he saw people as they really were. They all appeared to him so similar, with the same kind of body. They also had the same yearnings, fears and anxieties, craving for the same affection and love.

He realised that they all needed each other for their survival. They shared a common destiny and, although they addressed God by different names, all were sons and daughters of the same God the Father. That is why he was shocked and saddened to see such a hate-filled, power-crazy and self-centred world.

"My little ones", he said, "love one another! You have heard it said: 'Love your friends and hate your enemies'. Now I say to you: 'Love your enemies and pray for those who persecute you, so that you will become the children of your Father in heaven. For he makes the sun shine on bad and good people alike and gives rain to those who do good and to those who do evil. Why should God reward you if you love only the people who love you? Even sinners do that!'"

The crowds who heard him were infuriated. They

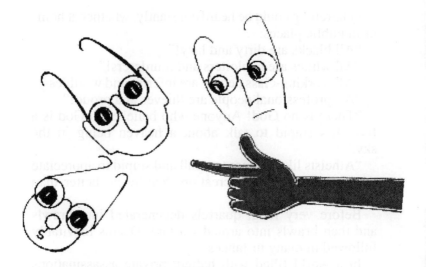

continued to insist that they were not the same and could not possibly have the same father:

"How can Jews be like Arabs? Blacks like whites? Foreigners like nationals?"

"Rich and poor can never be the same!" yelled others. "Communists and capitalists will always be different. You're talking nonsense!"

"You must be perfect," he resumed telling them, "just as your father in heaven is perfect. Love others as you love yourselves. Do to others what you would like others do to you. Remove your distorting spectacles and see the good that is in others."

"Rubbish!" the crowds continued to yell. "The man's nothing but a trouble-maker!"

"Traitor!"

"Don't let him get away with it!"

"Come on, let's silence him once and for all!"

It seemed that, for the first time in the history of the world, everyone was united. Although the various racial and religious groups had been torn apart for as long as anyone could remember, they all spontaneously joined together against a common enemy.

Jews and Romans, rich and poor, sinners and just, young and old, soldiers and civilians – they all now spoke, or rather yelled, with one voice:

"Crucify him! Crucify him!"

They did indeed crucify him, because he was too dangerous and because he had dared to look at the world and its inhabitants without distorting spectacles.

"God, my Father, forgive them all!" he cried from the cross to which they had nailed him. "They lost their sight. Their vision is distorted and they cannot see reality. Forgive them, Father! They don't really know what they're doing."

Almost twenty centuries have rolled by since that day. Quarrels have persisted. Resentment and hatred show no signs of abating. Wars have multiplied and many innocent people are still being liquidated. For how long will this continue?

GENERAL SUGGESTIONS

Messages of the parable

- Formation and transmission of prejudices.
- We are all affected by prejudices of various kinds: national, cultural, social, sexual, religious, etc.
- Without our realising it, prejudices become second nature to us.
- Prejudices colour our perceptions of reality and condition our thinking processes, determining emotional and behavioural patterns.
- We see Christ as a man free from prejudice.
- In order to follow Christ, we must shed our prejudices.
- We need honestly to accept that our prejudices, like our habits, die hard.
- In the fight against prejudice, even if it entails perception and social extinction, courage is needed: first within ourselves and then in our society.
- Being free from prejudice himself, Christ became an object of prejudice.

Ideas and applications of the parable

- Everyone is born free from prejudice.
- Our parents, teachers, elders and friends condition the way we think and we then start seeing things in a biased way.
- Intellectual and emotional prejudices are developed as our minds become stereotyped. We surrender our freedom of creativity or lose our vision of reality, replacing them with the intellectual and emotional prejudices attributable to the culture, class, ethnic group or religious affiliation into which we are born.
- These prejudices then blur and distort our vision, because we see life through spectacles tinted by our peculiar biases.
- We must beware of many dangerous prejudices, involving societies, nations, regions, languages, cultures, religions, social classes, ethnic groups, sex, colour, politics, families, etc.
- Prejudices condition us so much that we cannot see things and people as they are. We cannot feel, think and act objectively, because our rigid mental and psychological processes mould our lives into fixed patterns.
- Christ showed the way to love and accept all without prejudice.
- He taught us that we have a common Father and that we are all, without distinction, sisters and brothers.
- He taught us to love others as we love ourselves. For him, there were no Jews or Gentiles, rich or poor, friends or enemies, no just or sinners, no grown-ups or children. All were equal in his eyes. He loved and helped all, mixed with and talked with all.
- To be true disciples of Christ, we must fight prejudices with all our will and determination.
- If, like Christ, we want to love all, respect, accept and welcome all, we must be ready to be hated, persecuted and condemned, to be nailed to the cross of a world heavily biased against us.

New Testament texts in keeping with the ideas of the parable

1. Jesus's preaching:

Mt 5:21-26	Teaching about anger. Respect for people.
Mt 5:38-42	One should never take revenge against anybody but should return hurt with love. Love goes beyond the demands of strict justice.
Mt 25:31-46	Our relationship with God is proved by our relationship with any of our brothers and sisters.
Mk 3:31-35	Who is my mother and my brother and my sister? Anyone!
Mk 7:14-23	What makes a person unclean? Everybody's heart is the same. External things do not make us different.
Mk 9:35-37	Who is the greatest? Anyone who make themselves like children.
Mk 12:28-34	Which is the greatest commandment? To love God and all other people.
Lk 6:26-36	Love, even your enemies.
Lk 6:37-42	Do not judge anyone. Accept all.
Lk 10:25-37	The Good Samaritan. Everyone is your neighbour.
Lk 18:9-14	God looks at people's hearts, not at their actions.

2. Jesus's Practice:

Jesus does not make any distinction in the way he deals with:

Sinners and Just

Jn 8:1-11	The woman taken in adultery.
Lk 7:36-50	The sinful woman in the house of Simon.

Tax collectors and Pharisees

Lk 5:27-32	The call of Matthew.
Lk 19:1-10	Jesus goes to Zacchaeus's house.

Samaritans and Jews

Jn 4: 1-42	The Samaritan woman.
Lk 17:11-19	The Samaritan leper.

Foreigners and nationals

Lk 7:1-10	The Roman officer.
Mk 7:24-30	The Phoenician woman.

Women and men

Lk 10:38-42	Martha and Mary.
Lk 7:11-15	The widow of Nain.
Jn 20:11-18	Mary Magdalene.

Children and adults

Mk 10:13-16	"Let little children come to me."
Mt 18:2-6	Setting a child in their midst.

Poor and the rich

Mt 9:35-38	He has pity for the crowds.
Lk 7:36-38	Dining at the house of a rich Pharisee.

Uneducated and educated

Mk 1:14-20	Choosing his disciples – fishermen.
Jn 3:1-17	Jesus and Nicodemus.

3. Jesus an object of prejudice:

Free from prejudice, Jesus himself became an object of prejudice:

Mk 2:13-17	The call of Matthew.
Mk 3:1-6	The cure of the man with a crippled hand.
Mk 3:20-28	Jesus and Beelzebul.
Mk 6:1-6	Jesus is rejected at Nazareth.
Mk 7:1-13	The teaching of the ancestors.
Mt 26:57-67	Jesus before the Council.

Mt 27:15-26	Jesus is sentenced to death.
Lk 7:36-39	In the house of Simon the Pharisee.
Lk 19:1-10	At Zacchaeus's house.
Jn 9:1-41	The healing of the blind man. (A chapter on prejudice!)
Jn 11:45-54	The plot
Jn 12:9-11	against Jesus.
Jn 18:38-40	The death
Jn 19:1-22	of Jesus.

4. Other New Testament texts:

Col 3:8-11	There are no Gentiles and Jews... slaves and free...
Jas 2:1-13	Warning against prejudice.
Jas 2:14-26	Faith in action.
1 Jn 2:7-11	A new commandment.
1 Jn 3:11-18	Love one another.